It's a Jungle Out There

By S. Francis, H. Dugmore & Rico

David Philip Publishers

Cape Town & Johannesburg

Published 1998 in southern Africa by
David Philip Publishers (Pty) Ltd
208 Werdmuller Centre, Claremont 7700
in association with Rapid Phase
Johannesburg

ISBN 0-86486-411-6

Cover painting by   Annette Schacherl

Reproduction by Syreline Process
Printed by Creda Communications (Pty) Ltd
Eliot Avenue, Epping Industria, Cape Town, South Africa

"FIVE CHEERS FOR MADAM & EVE"
"South Africa's most successful cartoon strip
has won the hearts of millions."
– *The Mail & Guardian*

" LOCATES THE COMMON NATIONAL FUNNY BONE"
"Pokes fun across the lines of colour and caste …
widely published and widely quoted."
– *The Washington Post*

"DELICIOUSLY IRONIC"
"More than a book to enjoy – it's a collector's item …
Madam & Eve's creators clearly have their fingers
spot on the pulse of South African life."
– *The Citizen*

**"THE MOST PAINLESS WAY OF UNDERSTANDING
SOUTH AFRICAN POLITICS"**
– *The Guardian, London*

"AT LAST, IT'S TIME FOR A LAUGH"
"People of all colours and political stripe
can't get enough of Madam & Eve."
– *Newsweek Magazine*

**"FOR SHEER WIT AND SOPHISTICATED HUMOUR,
THERE IS NOTHING IN SOUTH AFRICA
TO TOUCH MADAM & EVE"**
"… Can take its place alongside the world's best cartoon
annuals – Giles, Andy Capp, Peanuts, Hagar."
– *The Eastern Province Herald*

**"OUTRAGEOUSLY FUNNY … WITH UNERRING
HUMOUR AND INTELLIGENCE"**
"If you haven't already fallen in love with
Madam & Eve, this is a fine opportunity."
– *Cosmopolitan Magazine*

"DOWNRIGHT HILARIOUS"
"Madam & Eve is a bridge over which a
good chuckle can roll until the belly-laughs at our
idiosyncasies eventually are allowed free transport."
– *The Cape Times*

**"THE MOST POPULAR CARTOON IN
SOUTH AFRICA"**
"Humour repressed for years, makes
a giddy comeback."
– *The Wall Street Journal*

OTHER MADAM & EVE BOOKS

MADAM & EVE APPEARS REGULARLY IN:

TO CONTACT MADAM & EVE

MADAM & Eve

BY S. FRANCIS, H. DUGMORE & RICO

IT BEGAN WITH SEVERAL TELKOM EXECUTIVES AND MEMBERS OF PARLIAMENT.

ZAP!

UH-OH.

CHIEF BUTHELEZI WAS NEXT.

AHEM. I HAVE PREPARED A SPEECH.

ZAP

WHOOPS.

DALI THAMBO AND FELICIA FOLLOWED.

LET'S SEE WHAT OUR STUDIO AUDIENCE THINKS!

ZAP

QUICK! GO TO COMMERCIAL!

AND, OF COURSE EVERYONE SUSPECTED LOUIS LUYT FROM THE VERY BEGINNING.

TODAY RUGBY... TOMORROW-- THE WORLD!

ZAP

DAMN.

...PROTECTING SOUTH AFRICA FROM ILLEGAL ALIENS.

MADAMS in BLACK

Coming Soon To A Theatre Near You.

7

Panel 1: MADAM... ISN'T IT YOUR MOTHER'S **BIRTHDAY** TOMORROW? / YES. AND EVERY YEAR IT'S THE SAME THING... SHE STARTS HINTING, SO WE DON'T FORGET.

Panel 2: CAN YOU BELIEVE IT? I FORGOT TODAY'S **DATE**. I MUST BE GETTING OLD.

Panel 3: REMEMBERING THE DATE USED TO BE A **PIECE OF CAKE**. I GUESS I'VE BEEN BURNING THE **CANDLE** AT BOTH ENDS.

Panel 4: SHE'S SHAMELESS. / AFTER ALL, I WASN'T **BORN** YESTERDAY.

Panel 5: :CLICK:

Panel 6: SURPRISE!! HAPPY BIRTHDAY!!

Panel 7: :CLICK:

Panel 8: MOM ALWAYS HATED SURPRISE PARTIES.

Panel 9: HAPPY BIRTHDAY GRANDMA. / THANK YOU ERIC. ...AND JUST WHAT I ALWAYS WANTED - A BOTTLE OF GIN.

Panel 10: ONE THING ABOUT MOM... SHE'S **EASY** TO SHOP FOR. / NEXT.

8

MADAM & EVE

BY S. FRANCIS, H. DUGMORE & RICO

THANKS FOR TAKING ME TO THE ZOO TO SEE **MAX**, MOTHER ANDERSON.

ZOO ENTRANCE

YEAH, RIGHT. JUST GO THROUGH THE METAL DETECTOR.

HEY! THAT'S NOT MAX! THAT'S A CARDBOARD CUT-OUT! WHERE'S MAX?!

WHO WANTS TO KNOW?

WE DO! WE DROVE **ALL** THE WAY HERE AND **PAID** OUR MONEY! NOW **WHERE** ARE ALL THE ANIMALS?!

OKAY, OKAY! CALM DOWN! THINGS ARE A LITTLE **TENSE** AROUND HERE SINCE THE **SHOOTING** INCIDENT. ...THEY'RE ALL OVER AT THE POLAR BEAR PIT.

BLAM! BLAM! BLAM!

I'M **OUT**. GIVE ME ANOTHER CLIP.

HEY - GET YOUR **OWN** AMMO.

GO AHEAD ...MAKE MY DAY.

TRY THE .38. YOU CAN'T BEAT IT FOR STOPPING POWER.

FITS RIGHT IN MY PAW, TOO.

10

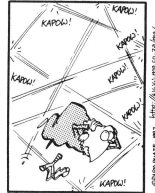

11

Row 1

HI. I'M MADAM.

AND I'M EVE.

NOW THAT OUR CARTOON IS SEEN ALL OVER THE WORLD... WE'VE BEEN GETTING LOTS OF MAIL ASKING US SPECIFIC QUESTIONS ABOUT SOUTH AFRICAN CULTURE.

...QUESTIONS LIKE... "WHAT IS A MIELIE LADY?"

...OR "WHO ARE THE TOKOLOSHES?"

WELL, THIS WEEK -- FOR OUR INTERNATIONAL READERS -- WE'LL BE ANSWERING ALL THOSE QUESTIONS.

I'LL BE HAPPY TO EXPLAIN THE CONCEPT OF "MIELIE LADIES."

Row 2

THIS WEEK ONLY!

MADAM & EVE'S SOUTH AFRICAN CULTURE... EXPLAINED FOR OUR INTERNATIONAL READERS

LESSON № 1: WHAT IS A MIELIE LADY?

THIS IS A "MIELIE LADY". SHE SELLS "MIELIES." YOU MIGHT CALL IT... "CORN" OR "MAIZE."

MIELLIES!!

LESSON № 2: THIS IS A "KATTY." YOU MIGHT CALL IT... A "SLINGSHOT."

MOM!

Row 3

SPECIAL FOR OUR INTERNATIONAL READERS!

MADAM & EVE'S SOUTH AFRICAN CULTURE FOR DUMMIES

LESSON № 3: HOW MUCH IS A RAND WORTH IN OTHER MONEY?

THIS IS A SOUTH AFRICAN RAND. RIGHT NOW, IT IS WORTH 5.80 TO THE US DOLLAR.

THIS IS A SOUTH AFRICAN RAND. IT IS NOW WORTH 5.90 TO THE US DOLLAR...

MOM!

BY POPULAR DEMAND!

MADAM & EVE'S

SOUTH AFRICAN CULTURE EXPLAINED

FOR OUR INTERNATIONAL READERS

LESSON Nº 4: THE BLACK GUYS ON THE BACK OF THE TRUCK...

LOTS OF PEOPLE ASK US ABOUT BLACK GUYS RIDING ON THE BACK OF TRUCKS. --WHO ARE THEY? WHAT DO THEY DO?

OBVIOUSLY, THEIR JOB IS TO ENTERTAIN BORED WHITE DRIVERS WITH FEATS OF GYMNASTICS DURING RUSH HOUR.

MOM!

I CAN'T HELP IT. THOSE FOREIGN READERS WILL BELIEVE ANYTHING!

MADAM & EVE'S

SOUTH AFRICAN CULTURE EXPLAINED FOR INTERNATIONAL READERS

LESSON Nº 5: CRIME

PEOPLE ALWAYS WRITE TO US AND ASK IF CRIME IS REALLY A PROBLEM IN SOUTH AFRICA.

THE ANSWER IS NO. FOREIGNERS HAVE ABSOLUTELY NOTHING TO WORRY ABOUT. WHEN VISITING SOUTH AFRICA, GO ANYWHERE YOU WANT, AND BRING ALL YOUR CASH AND VALUABLES.

... CAN WE MOVE TO THE NEXT LESSON, NOW, PLEASE?!

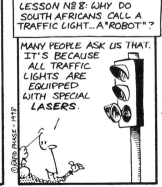

14

SOUTH AFRICAN CULTURE EXPLAINED FOR INTERNATIONAL READERS

LESSON Nº 9: WHAT EXACTLY IS "BILTONG"?

"BILTONG"... IS ACTUALLY DRIED, CURED MEAT.

IN AMERICA IT'S CALLED "BEEF JERKY" AND IS EATEN BY SOLDIERS OR PEOPLE TRAPPED IN THE WILDERNESS. BUT HERE IN SOUTH AFRICA, IT'S CONSIDERED A **DELICACY**.

...GO FIGURE.

MOM!

MORE SOUTH AFRICAN CULTURE EXPLAINED FOR INTERNATIONAL READERS

LESSON Nº 10: WHAT EXACTLY IS A "TOKOLOSHE"?

ACCORDING TO LEGEND, A "TOKOLOSHE" IS A SMALL MYTHICAL DEMON THAT CARRIES AWAY PEOPLE WHILE THEY'RE ASLEEP.

WHAT MANY PEOPLE DON'T KNOW, HOWEVER, IS THAT THEY'RE ALSO EXCELLENT CHESS PLAYERS.

CHECKMATE.

HEY! WAIT! I WAS ABOUT TO EXPLAIN "SANGOMAS" NEXT!

15

16

MADAM & Eve

BY S. FRANCIS, H. DUGMORE & RICO

YOUR LANGUAGE TEACHER IS HERE FOR YOUR LESSON, MISTER PRESIDENT.

GOOD. SHOW HIM IN.

PARLEZ-VOUS FRANCAIS, MONSIEUR PRESIDENT?

OUI, YEBO.

SORRY TO INTERRUPT YOUR LESSON, MISTER PRESIDENT, BUT I NEED YOUR APPROVAL ON THESE **TRAVEL REQUISITIONS**.

...TRAVEL REQUISITIONS?

YES, SIR. IT SEEMS OVER 92% OF YOUR CABINET HAVE REQUESTED TO ATTEND AN IMPORTANT OVERSEAS CONFERENCE ON **BLUE CHEESE**.

92% OF MY CABINET WANT TO ATTEND A CONFERENCE ON BLUE CHEESE? **WHERE?!** ...**WHEN?!**

PARIS, FRANCE, SIR. IN JUNE NEXT YEAR.

PARIS... JUNE? ISN'T THAT THE EXACT SAME TIME SOUTH AFRICA PLAYS IN THE **SOCCER WORLD CUP**?

YOU'RE RIGHT, **SIR**. IT **IS** AN INCREDIBLE COINCIDENCE.

NEVERTHELESS... WE SHOULDN'T UNDERESTIMATE THE IMPORTANCE OF BLUE CHEESE ON A GLOBAL LEVEL.

LET ME PUT IT THIS WAY, SIR. I THINK YOU SHOULD ATTEND ALSO.

BY THE WAY... IS THAT A **FRENCH BERET** YOU'RE WEARING?

YOU LIKE IT, SIR? I BORROWED IT FROM THABO.

17

WRENCH.

ARE YOU **SURE** EVE KNOWS HOW TO FIX YOUR CAR?

OF COURSE! WHAT **ELSE** COULD SHE BE DOING UNDER THERE FOR TWO HOURS?

YOU'VE DECIDED TO SELL YOUR CAR, MADAM?

THAT'S RIGHT, EVE. I'VE ALREADY PUT THE AD IN THE PAPER.

FOR SALE

"MINT CONDITION ... LOW MILEAGE ... ONLY DRIVEN BY A LITTLE OLD LADY EVERY SUNDAY."

"... DRIVEN BY A LITTLE OLD LADY EVERY SUNDAY?"

YOU SAID SOMETHING ABOUT AN **ACTING** JOB?

MOM -- IF I'M GOING TO **SELL** MY CAR, WE'VE GOT TO PRACTICE. I'LL BE "THE CUSTOMER" -- AND **YOU** BE THE "LITTLE OLD LADY WHO ONLY DROVE IT ON SUNDAYS."

HMM. NICE CAR ... SO **YOU'RE** THE LITTLE OLD LADY WHO ONLY DROVE THE CAR ON SUNDAYS.

THAT'S RIGHT.

AND *WHERE* DID YOU DRIVE IT ON SUNDAYS?

KYALAMI RACETRACK.

CHURCH! YOU WENT TO CHURCH!!

NOBODY HAS A SENSE OF HUMOUR AROUND HERE.

MOTHER ANDERSON ENTERS HER FAVOURITE SOAP OPERA...

LOOK OFFICER! THIS WOMAN HAS BEEN **DRINKING!** SHE DOESN'T KNOW WHAT SHE'S SAYING!

BESIDES... I CAN **PROVE** I'M NOT HAVING AN AFFAIR! JUST ASK OUR MAID!

MAID??

©RAPID PHASE—1997 http://wukuki.mg.co.za/mg/

EVA! ...THANK GOODNESS!

YOU WANTED TO SEE ME, SIR?

HEY!! THIS IS **MY** FANTASY!

NOT ANYMORE.

MOTHER ANDERSON ENTERS HER FAVOURITE TV SOAP...

OKAY! ÷CHOKE÷ I ADMIT EVERYTHING! I'M HAVING AN **AFFAIR** WITH MY **SECRETARY!**

©RAPID PHASE—1997 http://wukuki.mg.co.za/mg/

BUT THAT'S NOT ALL! I **ALSO** KNOW WHO MURDERED MY HALF-SISTER'S ILLEGITIMATE BROTHER'S STEPMOTHER!

THIS IS GETTING GOOD.

THE IDENTITY OF THE MURDERER IS...IS...

WHO? ...WHO?!

♫ YOU HAVE AN UNCLE IN THE FURNITURE BUSINESS!! ♫ ♫ ♫

GREAT. ...AN ADVERT.

21

GET OUT OF MY FACE.

I LEARNED THAT AT SCHOOL TODAY.

HEY YOU! GET OUT OF MY FACE!

ACTUALLY... IT DOESN'T MAKE SENSE! HOW CAN YOU BE IN SOMEBODY'S FACE?

OH, YOU'D BE SURPRISED.

DO PEOPLE GET IN YOUR FACE OFTEN?

MORE THAN YOU KNOW.

IS CHIEF BUTHELEZI EVER IN YOUR FACE?

DEFINITELY.

DOES FELICIA MABUZA-SUTTLE GET IN YOUR FACE?

CONSTANTLY.

FW DE KLERK?

NOT ANYMORE.

WHAT ABOUT ME? AM I EVER IN YOUR FACE?

NO COMMENT.

MAYBE THEY SHOULD CALL SOUTH AFRICA... "THE RAINBOW NATION IN YOUR FACE."

I'LL NOTIFY THE OLYMPIC COMMITTEE.

MADAM & EVE

BY S. FRANCIS, H. DUGMORE & RICO

LAST CALL, GUYS. IT'S ALMOST CLOSING TIME.

BOB's BAR & FONDUE

HEY-- AREN'T YOU LUCIANO PAVAROTTI, BJORN BORG AND NELSON MANDELA ?!

NO!

NO!

ATHENS!! I CAN'T **BELIEVE** THEY GAVE THE 2004 OLYMPICS TO ATHENS!

... AND AFTER ALL I DID! I SANG ALL THE JUDGES A **PRIVATE ARIA** FROM "RIGOLETTO"... AND I MADE THEM ALL SPAGHETTI!!

... **YOU ?!** WHAT ABOUT **ME** ?! I GAVE EVERY ONE OF THE JUDGES A **PRIVATE TENNIS LESSON!**

... AND YOU, NELSON?

ᴈGROANᴈ I GAVE EACH JUDGE AN **AFRICAN SHIRT** AND TAUGHT THEM ALL TO **TOYI-TOYI!**

THEN **HOW** IN THE WORLD DID ATHENS GET IT? WE'RE BIG CELEBRITIES!!

EXCUSE ME, CAN I GET A DOUBLE OUZO... ANOTHER LARGE BEER FOR HERCULES AND A CAMPARI AND SODA FOR APHRODITE.

COMING RIGHT UP, ZEUS.

THANKS BOB.

OH YEAH? WHO WANTS TO STEP OUTSIDE AND HIT A FEW BALLS?!!

CALM DOWN, BJORN.

© RICO BASE 1997

26

MADAM & Eve

BY S. FRANCIS, H. DUGMORE & RICO

LISTEN TO THIS, MOM. YOU WERE LOOKING FOR A PART-TIME JOB:" GET INTO THE IMPORT-EXPORT BUSINESS! STAY OVERNIGHT IN EXOTIC COLOMBIA. FLY HOME NEXT DAY. ALL EXPENSES PAID!

"...ABILITY TO SWALLOW LARGE OBJECTS WHOLE, A BIG PLUS."

HELLO? IS MISTER ABATCHA HERE?

WHO WANTS TO KNOW?

ABC IMPORT EXPORT

I DO. EDITH ANDERSON. I'M ANSWERING YOUR AD IN THE PAPER FOR AN IMPORT/EXPORT REPRESENTATIVE.

AHA.

HERE. HAVE A HARD BOILED EGG.

THANK YOU. DON'T MIND IF I DO.

CAN YOU SWALLOW IT WITHOUT CHEWING?

PARDON ME?

IT'S A TEST FOR ALL OUR NEW EMPLOYEES. WE WANT TO SEE IF YOU CAN SWALLOW IT AND THEN RETRIEVE IT THE NEXT DAY.

RETRIEVE IT?! HOW CAN I POSSIBLY RETRIEVE SOMETHING I SWALLOWED?!

BSSST. BSSST. BSSST.

©RICO PHASE-1997

RETRIEVE THIS!!

BONK!

HOW WAS THE IMPORT-EXPORT JOB, MOM?

THE IMPORT PART WAS OKAY. IT WAS THE EXPORT PART I COULDN'T STOMACH.

YOU MUST BE JOKING! WHY ON EARTH WOULD I NEED SUPER GLUE SOLVENT?

SUPER GLUE SOLVENT
Only 10 Rand

SUPER GLUE SOLVENT
Only 10 Rand

WILL THAT BE CASH, CHEQUE OR CREDIT CARD?

SUPER GLUE SOLVENT
Only 10 Rand

UH,... MOSCOW. WE HAVE A PROBLEM.

MIELLLIES!!

SSSSSSST!

AAAAAH!!

OKAY. FIFTY-FIFTY SPLIT.

MIELIE LADY REPELLANT
Only 50 Rand

29

DON'T YOU THINK THIS IS AN AMAZING COINCIDENCE, EVE? YOU'RE DATING SOMEONE NAMED "ADAM"... THAT MAKES YOU "ADAM & EVE".

US? WAIT A MINUTE! WHAT ABOUT YOU TWO? YOU'RE "MADAM & EVE".

I DON'T GET IT.

THIS IS AMAZING. OVER HERE WE HAVE "ADAM & EVE..."

...OR "MADAM & EVE." IS THIS AN AMAZING COINCIDENCE OR WHAT?

HI, I'M SADDAM. I'VE JUST ARRIVED FROM IRAQ.

IF YOU ASK ME, THE WRITERS ARE REALLY STRETCHING THIS PREMISE.

ISN'T THIS AMAZING, MOM? WHEREVER MICHAEL JACKSON PERFORMS, THEY PUT UP THIS GIANT STATUE TO PROMOTE HIS TOUR.

DOESN'T LOOK TOO STURDY IF YOU ASK ME.

LOOK OUT! HIS NOSE IS LOOSE!

CRASH!

MOM... ARE YOU OKAY?

THAT'S IT. I'M SUING.

AND IN OTHER NEWS, AN ELDERLY WOMAN WAS SLIGHTLY INJURED YESTERDAY, WHEN THE GIANT **NOSE** OF THE **MICHAEL JACKSON** STATUE INEXPLICABLY CAME LOOSE...

...AND PLUMMETED TO THE GROUND, LANDING PARTIALLY ON THE WOMAN'S FOOT.

WHEN HE HEARD OF THE INCIDENT, MICHAEL TOOK TIME OFF HIS BUSY SCHEDULE TO STOP BY THE HOSPITAL AND CHEER THE WOMAN UP.

I LOVE YOU. HAVE A TEDDY BEAR.

GIVE IT TO MY LAWYER.

HELLO. I'M MICHAEL JACKSON'S **ATTORNEY**.

I UNDERSTAND YOU'RE CLAIMING THAT THE ALLEGED GIANT NOSE FROM MICHAEL'S STATUE ALLEGEDLY FELL ON YOUR FOOT, AND YOU WERE ALLEGEDLY INJURED.

ALLEGEDLY?!! WHAT DO YOU CALL **THIS**?!!

AN ALLEGED BANDAGE.

I HATE LAWYERS.

MADAM & EVE

BY S. FRANCIS, H. DUGMORE & RICO

MIELLLLLIES!!

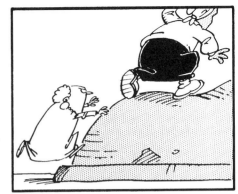

MIELLLLIES!!

OH, SHUT UP.

MADAM & EVE

BY S. FRANCIS, H. DUGMORE & RICO

CAN YOU BELIEVE THIS? WINNIE'S MAKING A BID TO BE ANC DEPUTY PRESIDENT!

WHAT'S NEXT? ...DEPUTY PRESIDENT OF THE COUNTRY?!

CAN YOU IMAGINE IF NELSON STAYS IN OFFICE? HIS EX-WIFE COULD BE DEPUTY-PRESIDENT?

SOUNDS LIKE A TELEVISION SITUATION COMEDY.

GRACA HONEY! I'M HOME!

NELSON! HOW WAS YOUR DAY?

©RAPID PHASE 1997

TERRIBLE! I GOT BACK FROM A MEETING AND FOUND OUT WINNIE RE-INSTATED THE DEATH PENALTY!

HAHAHA! HOOHOO! HEEHEE HAHAHA! HEEH HOHOHO HAHA

THAT'S ODD. I THOUGHT I HEARD CANNED LAUGHTER.

DINNER'S ALMOST READY, DEAR.

FORGET DINNER! GET ME A DOUBLE SCOTCH!

BUT NELSON... YOU DON'T DRINK!

I DO NOW!

HAHAHA! HEHEHE! HEEHEEHEE! HEEHEEHEE! HOOHOOHOO!

AND THAT'S NOT ALL! WINNIE JUST HIRED SOME MORE BODY-GUARDS AND WENT ON A TRIP AROUND THE WORLD AT TAXPAYER'S EXPENSE!

HAHAHA! HEEHEE! HEEHEE! HOOHOO! HAWHAW! HA-HA-HA! HEE-HEE! HEEH

BUT NELSON-- WHAT ABOUT THE TRUTH & RECONCILIATION COMMISSION?! CAN'T THEY DO SOMETHING?!

NOT ANYMORE. BISHOP TUTU'S BEEN KIDNAPPED.

HEEHEE! HOHOHO! HAWHAW! HAHAHA! HEEHEEHEE! CLAPCLAPCLAP CLAP CLAPCLAP CLAP

AND WE'LL BE RIGHT BACK WITH MORE OF... "MADIBA AND THE DEPUTY"... AFTER THIS.

MADAM & EVE'S
RAINBOW NATION MAGIC
COMPLETE CATALOGUE OF SOUTH AFRICAN MAGIC TRICKS AND ILLUSIONS

BE THE LIFE OF THE PARTY! AMAZE YOUR FRIENDS!

THE ESCAPING PRISONER

A PRISONER IS ARRESTED, HANDCUFFED AND INCARCERATED IN A PRISON CELL. TURN YOUR BACK... AND POOF!

HE'S GONE!

WHERE DID HE GO?! WHO KNOWS?!

Only 69.95

MIRACLE GOLDEN OLYMPIC RINGS

JUST WHEN YOU THOUGHT YOU HAVE THEM ALL LINED UP AND HOOKED TOGETHER, THEY COMPLETELY DISAPPEAR!

TRULY ASTOUNDING!!

Only 49.95

THE DISAPPEARING CBD

YOU'VE SEEN MAGICIAN DAVID COPPERFIELD VANISH A 747 JET AND THE STATUE OF LIBERTY... NOW YOU CAN MAKE AN ENTIRE CENTRAL BUSINESS DISTRICT DISAPPEAR! AN INCREDIBLE ILLUSION!

Also available... the disappearing Premier.

Only 54.95

THE INDESTRUCTIBLE WOMAN ILLUSION!!

A WOMAN VOLUNTEER FROM THE AUDIENCE -- SAY, DR ZUMA OR WINNIE MADIKIZELA MANDELA -- IS ESCORTED ON STAGE AND PLACED IN A LARGE CABINET. YET, NO MATTER HOW MANY **SPIKES, SWORDS AND NAILS** ARE THRUST THROUGH, PINNING HER DOWN, THE WOMAN **ESCAPES UNHARMED!!**

MUST BE SEEN TO BE BELIEVED!

Only 1470.00

MAGICAL MONEY

AN ORDINARY TEN RAND NOTE IS PUT IN AN ENVELOPE AND MAILED AT THE POST OFFICE. AMAZINGLY IT **NEVER** REACHES ITS DESTINATION! WORKS EVERY TIME! Only 20.95

THE MYSTERIOUS RE-APPEARING DRIVER'S LICENCE

DEFIES THE LAWS OF PHYSICS! A DRIVER'S LICENCE SUDDENLY DISAPPEARS -- ONLY TO RE-APPEAR IN A PARLIAMENTARIAN'S PURSE MANY HUNDREDS OF KILOMETRES AWAY!

FOOLS PRACTICALLY EVERYONE!!

Only 69.95

MADIBA·MAGIC

RUGBY JERSEY

SIMPLY PUT ON THIS MAGIC JERSEY... AND PRESTO!! YOUR FAVOURITE SPORTS TEAM WINS THE WORLD CUP!

TRULY ASTONISHING!

Only 168·95

THE VANISHING CAR

AMAZING A SPECTATOR'S LUXURY CAR IS PARKED ON A BUSY STREET CORNER. THIRTY SECONDS LATER... IT'S GONE! -- ONLY TO REAPPEAR LATER IN ZIMBABWE WITH A NEW COLOUR AND REGISTRATION!

YOU WON'T BELIEVE IT! Only 1995.00

The Levitating RAND

SAY A FEW MAGIC WORDS... AND WATCH AN ORDINARY FIFTY RAND NOTE **LEVITATE**! YOU WON'T BELIEVE YOUR OWN EYES!

(UNFORTUNATELY, IT ONLY LEVITATES **DOWNWARDS**.)

Only 59.95

THE DISAPPEARING SUGAR

GOING... GOING... **GONE!** A FULL BAG OF SUGAR MYSTERIOUSLY VANISHES RIGHT BEFORE YOUR EYES! WHERE DID IT GO?!

Also Available: Disappearing Coffee

Only 12.95

38

Row 1:

DAVID COPPERFIELD'S HERE TO SEE YOU, SIR.

GOOD, SHOW HIM IN.

DAVID!

MISTER PRESIDENT!

THANK YOU FOR COMING HERE TO TEACH ME MORE "MADIBA MAGIC."

MY PLEASURE! SO... WHAT TRICK WOULD YOU LIKE TO WORK ON FIRST?

THE DISAPPEARING EX-WIFE.

UH, WHY DON'T WE START WITH A FEW SIMPLE CARD TRICKS...

Row 2:

TRUST ME, MISTER PRESIDENT... FOR YOUR "MADIBA MAGIC" SHOW, YOU'VE GOT TO THINK BIG!

ON MY DAVID COPPERFIELD TV SPECIAL I MADE A BOEING 747 DISAPPEAR. I MADE THE STATUE OF LIBERTY DISAPPEAR!

ARE THERE ANY FAMOUS SOUTH AFRICAN LANDMARKS YOU'D LIKE TO MAKE DISAPPEAR?

YES. WE CAN START WITH THE VOOR-TREKKER MONUMENT.

OKAY. NOW YOU'RE TALKING.

Row 3:

YOU WANTED TO SEE ME, MISTER PRESIDENT?

YES. I HAVE THE REVISED SCHEDULE FOR TONIGHT'S "MADIBA MAGIC" STATE DINNER.

7:00 PM — I'M INTRODUCED

7:01 PM — I GIVE A BRIEF SPEECH ON THE RAINBOW NATION.

7:15 PM — I DO A FEW CARD TRICKS.

7:30 PM —... I SAW THE CUBAN AMBASSADOR IN HALF.

SOUNDS LIKE A FUN EVENING, SIR.

41

MADAM... I CAN'T FIND YOUR MOTHER ANYWHERE IN THE HOTEL!

I THINK SHE SNUCK INTO THE **FIRST ANNUAL MIELIE LADY CONVENTION.**

WELL, AT LEAST SHE CAN'T DO ANY HARM. I TOOK AWAY HER **KATTY.**

MIELLLIES! OW!!

PTOO!

©RAPID PHASE 1997

AND NOW, THE **FIRST ANNUAL MIELIE LADY CONVENTION** WOULD LIKE TO INTRODUCE OUR **GUEST SPEAKER...**

FAMOUS MOTIVATIONAL EXPERT-- **BOB POWER!**

HI THERE!

LET'S GET MOTIVATED!!

MIELIE LADIES AND MOTIVATIONAL SPEAKERS ... SO MANY TARGETS ... SO LITTLE TIME.

HUH?

PTING!

PTOO!

http://www.mg.co.za/mg/   ©RAPID PHASE 1997

AND REMEMBER, MIELIE LADIES! IF YOU LOOK AT LIFE AND SEE **MAGIC** ...THEN YOU'LL BE A **MAGICIAN!**

BUT IF YOU LOOK AROUND AND ALL YOU SEE IS **TRAGEDY** ...THEN YOUR LIFE WILL BE **TRAGIC!**

SUPPOSE YOU LOOK AROUND AND SEE LOTS OF **MONEY?**

THEN YOU'LL BE A MOTIVATIONAL SPEAKER!

THERE'S ALWAYS SOMEONE IN THE AUDIENCE WITH A **BLOWGUN.**

BONK!

PTOO!

MADAM & EVE

BY S.FRANCIS, H.DUGMORE & RICO

HELLO. MY NAME IS GWEN ANDERSON... ...AND I SUFFER FROM ... ⸘CHOKE⸘ ...WINNIE PHOBIA.

HI, GWEN!!

⸘SOB⸘

THANK YOU, GWEN. THAT TOOK A LOT OF COURAGE.

WELCOME PEOPLE, TO OUR FIRST DE-SENSITIZING THERAPY SEMINAR. HOPEFULLY, BY THE END OF THE DAY, YOU'LL HAVE CONQUERED YOUR IRRATIONAL PHOBIA OF WINNIE MADIKIZELA MANDELA...

AAAAH!!

SORRY. I USED THE "W" WORD... I APOLOGISE.

⸘SOB⸘ ⸘MOAN⸘ ⸘CHOKE⸘

OKAY. LET'S MOVE SLOWLY. I HAVE HERE A BOTTLE OF SOIL, TAKEN FROM YOU-KNOW-WHO'S BACKYARD. WHO WANTS TO TOUCH IT?

OH, COME ON! IT'S JUST A BOTTLE OF SOIL! IT WON'T BITE!

GOOD! THAT'S IT! PUT YOUR FINGER ON IT.

©RAPID PHASE - 1997   http://www.mg.co.za/mg/

SPROINGGG!!

GASP!!

OKAY. SO MUCH FOR SHOCK THERAPY. LET'S LOOK AT THE VIDEO.

IT'S MY DAUGHTER, DOCTOR. SHE WAS IN FRONT OF THE TELEVISION... AND THEN SHE JUST STARTED SCREAMING.
THE TELEVISION? ...WHAT WAS SHE WATCHING?

I THINK IT WAS A NEWS SEGMENT... SOMETHING ABOUT WINNIE MADIKIZELA-MANDELA CAMPAIGNING FOR ANC DEPUTY PRESIDENT.

AAAAAH!!

IT'S WINNIE PHOBIA, ISN'T IT?
COMMON TO MOST WHITE PEOPLE. THERE'S A LOT OF IT GOING AROUND.

JUST RELAX, MRS. ANDERSON. I NEED TO RUN SOME TESTS.
YES, DOCTOR.

NELSON! ...THABO! ...JACOB! ...TOKYO!

...WINNIE!
AAAH!!

YEP. IT'S WINNIE PHOBIA, ALL RIGHT.
MAKE HER WELL! MONEY IS NO OBJECT!

MADAM IS DIAGNOSED WITH WINNIE PHOBIA...

OKAY, MRS. ANDERSON. I WANT YOU TO USE THE WORDS "WINNIE"... AND "DEPUTY PRESIDENT" IN THE SAME SENTENCE.

NO PROBLEM. WINNIE IS RUNNING FOR REPUTY DESIDENT.

I MEAN, WINNIE IS RUNNING FOR PEPUTY RESIDENT! SEPUDY PEDIMENT! RICKETY PEPSIDENT!

;CHOKE;
TAKE YOUR TIME. YOU CAN DO IT.

EVE SAYS YOU'RE TURNING INTO A COUCH POTATO. YOU SIT AROUND ALL DAY DOING NOTHING.

OH, SHE DID, DID SHE?

I ARGUED IN YOUR FAVOUR. #1 -- YOU DON'T EVEN SIT ON A COUCH. #2 -- I WOULDN'T CALL WATCHING SOAP OPERAS ON TV ALL DAY "...DOING NOTHING."

.. AND #3 -- YOU DON'T JUST SIT THERE... YOU GET UP LOTS OF TIMES TO REFILL YOUR GIN & TONIC.

I'M THINKING OF BECOMING A LAWYER.

HI! HOW ARE YOU?! I'M FINE!

HAHAHA! THAT'S A GOOD ONE! SO GOOD OF YOU TO CALL!

OKAY MOM. WE'RE ALONE NOW. YOU CAN STOP PRETENDING.

WHEN I FIND OUT WHO PUT SUPERGLUE ON MY CELLPHONE, I'LL KILL THEM.

MADAM & EVE

BY S. FRANCIS, H. DUGMORE & RICO

AND, AS THE WINNIE MADIKIZELA MANDELA HEARING APPEARS TO BE DEADLOCKED...THE TRUTH AND RECONCILIATION COMMISSION HAS CALLED IN TWO SURPRISE CRIMINAL CONSULTANTS AT THE LAST MINUTE.

I HOPE YOU KNOW WHAT YOU'RE DOING, SHERLOCK.

ELEMENTARY, MY DEAR EVE.

GOOD MORNING, BISHOP TUTU. ...I DEDUCE FROM THE PURPLE ON YOUR FROCK THAT YOU HAD GRAPE JAM FOR BREAKFAST.

WHAT ARE YOU TALKING ABOUT? I ALWAYS WEAR PURPLE!

THEN LET ME GET RIGHT TO THE CASE. AS I ALWAYS SAY... WHEN YOU REMOVE THE IMPOSSIBLE... WHATEVER'S LEFT -- NO MATTER HOW IMPROBABLE-- IS THE SOLUTION.

SO MANY WITNESSES...SO MANY CONFLICTING STORIES. ...BUT ONLY ONE PERSON IN THIS ROOM HAD MOTIVE... MEANS...AND OPPORTUNITY. AND THAT PERSON IS...

WINNIE MADIKIZELA MANDELA!! WINNIE IS GUILTY!!

GASP!!

...WHAT? MY DEDUCTION WAS WRONG?

GASP!

©RAPID PHASE-1997

WAIT A MINUTE! I KNOW WHO DID IT! I KNOW WHO DID IT, I TELL YOU!!

IT WAS COLONEL MUSTARD IN THE BILLIARD ROOM WITH THE CANDLE-STICK!!

ARE YOU SURE YOU'VE BEEN WATERING DOWN HER GIN & TONICS?

MADAM & EVE

BY S. FRANCIS, H. DUGMORE & RICO

THE TRUTH AND RECONCILIATION COMMISSION CALLS THE NEXT DEFENDANT.

STATE YOUR NAME FOR THE RECORD.

SANTA CLAUS.

IS YOUR LAWYER PRESENT?

PRESENT, MISTER CHAIRMAN! ...MISTER RUDOLPH OF THE FIRM DONNER, BLITZEN AND PRANCER.

MISTER RUDOLPH, YOUR CLIENT HAS BEEN ACCUSED OF NUMEROUS OFFENCES... CHIMNEY TRESPASSING... ELF EXPLOITATION AND REINDEER ABUSE.

MY CLIENT IS INNOCENT OF ALL CHARGES.

RIGHT. SWEAR IN THE NEXT WITNESS.

STATE YOUR NAME FOR THE RECORD.

ALFIE THE ELF.

MISTER ELF... HOW LONG HAVE YOU WORKED AT THE NORTH POLE?

TWO HUNDRED YEARS... THAT'S SEVEN DAYS A WEEK, EIGHTEEN HOURS A DAY!

AND HOW WOULD YOU CHARACTERIZE YOUR EMPLOYER, SANTA CLAUS?

HE THINKS HE'S A DEMIGOD! HE THINKS HE'S ABOVE THE LAW!

THE ELF'S CRAZY.

DON'T TELL ME I'M CRAZY! HIS HANDS ARE DRIPPING WITH THE SWEAT OF ELVES!!

© RICO PHALE - 1997

MISTER CHAIRMAN -- I MOVE FOR A RECESS! THE DEFENDANT IS INTIMIDATING THE WITNESS!

AGREED! CALL THE NEXT CASE!

...I NEVER STOLE THOSE TEETH! THEY WERE LEFT FOR ME UNDER THE PILLOW!

HURRY UP! YOU'RE MISSING THE TOOTH FAIRY!

56

IT'S STARTED, EVE... THE MYSTERIOUS DISAPPEARANCE OF EVERYONE DURING THE CHRISTMAS HOLIDAYS.

ONE MINUTE THERE'S PEOPLE EVERYWHERE... THEN... ≷POOF≷ EVERYONE VANISHES... ONLY TO RE-APPEAR IN JANUARY!

VERY FUNNY.

HA HA HA
HO HO HO
HEE HEE HEE

HOO HOO HOO
HAHAHA
HEEHEEHEE

'TIS THE SEASON TO BE JOLLY.

25 MORE DAYS TILL SCHOOL RE-OPENS.

I'M TELLING YOU MARGE...THIS TROPICAL ISLAND IS THE BEST KEPT SECRET HOLIDAY SPOT! IT'S LIKE A LOST WORLD HERE!

MADAM & EVE

BY S. FRANCIS, H. DUGMORE & RICO

QUICKLY! HIT THE GROUND!! AND KEEP AWAY FROM THE WINDOWS!!

WHO'S OUT THERE, MOM?! ...HIJACKERS? BURGLARS?

DUSTBIN MEN! THEY'RE COLLECTING FOR CHRISTMAS!

STEP ASIDE, MOM. LET'S JUST PAY THEM AND GET IT OVER WITH.

WHY?! WE CAN HOLD OUT LONGER THAN THEY CAN!

HI! WE'RE YOUR DUSTBIN MEN! MERRY CHRISTMAS!

NOT SO FAST!! HOW DO WE KNOW YOU'RE THE REAL DUSTBIN MEN... AND NOT IMPOSTERS!

OKAY. IT'S 7:30 ON A TUESDAY MORNING. DOES THIS SOUND FAMILIAR?

CLANG! CLANG! CLANG!

WHISTLE!

AYIYE! AYIYE! SHESHA!

BARK! BARK! BARK!

WOOF! WOOF! WOOF!

YAP! YAP! YAP!

PAY 'EM.

HEE HAW!

I'M AUDITIONING FOR THE ROLE OF THE DONKEY IN THE SCHOOL NATIVITY PLAY.

SLAM!
...OF COURSE, NOT EVERYONE APPRECIATES TRUE *ACTING* TALENT.

I CHANGED MY MIND. I'M NOW AUDITIONING FOR THE ROLE OF *MARY* IN THE SCHOOL NATIVITY PLAY.

THERE'S NO **ROOM** AT THE INN!!

THERE'S NO ROOM AT THE INN!!

LET ME BACK IN THE ROOM!!

THIS IS SO **HUMILIATING!** I AUDITIONED FOR THE SCHOOL NATIVITY PLAY -- AND MY TEACHER GAVE ME THE **WORST** ROLE POSSIBLE!

REMEMBER WHAT THEY SAY. EVERY ACTING ROLE IS A CHALLENGE.

WHAT CHALLENGE? I'M PLAYING THE **REAR** END OF A CAMEL!

YES, BUT CAN YOU BE A **BELIEVABLE** REAR END OF A CAMEL?

 JINGLE BELLS! CRIME RATE SWELLS, FOLKS ON HOLIDAY!

 OH WHAT FUN WHEN WE BREAK IN-- TO TAKE YOUR STUFF A-WAY!

 DASHING THROUGH THE STREETS, WHILE EVERYONE'S AWAY... OVER THE WALL WE GO, LAUGHING ALL THE WAY-- HAHAHAHAHA!

 THIS TIME OF THE YEAR, **EVERYONE** CATCHES THE CHRISTMAS SPIRIT.

WITH THANKS TO JOY PRETORIUS

 WE THREE KINGS FROM ORIENT ARE... BEARING GIFTS, WE TRAVELLED SO FAR...

 ARMED GUYS JUMPED US... PUNCHED AND KICKED US...

...AND LEFT US ON THE TAR.

 ...AND THAT'S WHAT HAPPENED, HONEST.

HERE'S YOUR CASE NUMBER. WE'LL GET BACK TO YOU.

DECK THE HALLS WITH **BUDDY HOLLY**, FA LA LA LA LA, LA LA LA LA.

ONLY 17 MORE DAYS LEFT TILL SCHOOL REOPENS.

HI! EVE SAID NOT TO BOTHER YOU THIS MORNING BECAUSE YOU OVERINDULGED LAST NIGHT.

WATCH THIS.

PLOP

I THOUGHT YOU SAID SHE'D BEEN THROWING UP AT THE DROP OF A HAT.

AS SOON AS I REGAIN THE USE OF MY LEGS, I'LL KILL BOTH OF THEM.

MADAM & Eve

BY S. FRANCIS, H. DUGMORE & RICO

HELLO... AND WELCOME TO THE FIRST PRISON WARDER REFRESHER COURSE. TODAY WE'LL BE COVERING -- "ESCAPES... AND HOW TO PREVENT THEM."

OKAY, LET'S START WITH THE BASICS. THIS... IS A LOCK.

I KNEW IT!

SO THAT'S WHAT THAT WAS!

OKAY, QUIET DOWN PEOPLE. THIS IS SIPHO. HE'S CURRENTLY DOING 20 YEARS FOR ARMED ROBBERY. HE'S AGREED TO HELP US WITH A LITTLE ROLE-PLAYING EXERCISE.

GO AHEAD, SIPHO.

I WANT TO ESCAPE! GIVE ME YOUR KEYS!

NO WAY!

GOOD!

I WANT TO ESCAPE! GIVE ME YOUR GUN!

NO WAY!

GOOD!

I WANT TO ESCAPE! GIVE ME YOUR KEYS, YOUR GUN... AND HERE'S TEN THOUSAND BUCKS.

NO WAY!

THE GOING RATE'S TWENTY THOUSAND!

OKAY! WHO SAID THAT?!

RIGHT, THEN. LET'S BREAK FOR TEA. AND LET'S GIVE SIPHO A BIG HAND FOR HELPING US.

CLAP CLAP CLAP CLAP CLAP CLAP CLAP CLAP CLAP CLAP

©RAPID PHASE-1997   http://www.mg.co.za/mg

HERE'S YOUR GIN & TONIC, MOTHER ANDERSON.

NO THANK YOU. I'VE DECIDED TO **GIVE THEM UP** FOR NEW YEAR'S.

VERY FUNNY.

I HEARD YOU GAVE UP DRINKING GIN & TONICS FOR NEW YEAR'S.

THAT'S RIGHT.

I BET THAT'S REALLY DIFFICULT, ISN'T IT?

NOT AT ALL. ACTUALLY IT'S EASIER THAN I THOUGHT.

WHAT'S IN THE GLASS?

TEQUILA.

CONGRATULATIONS, MOM. THIS IS YOUR THIRD DAY WITHOUT A GIN & TONIC. HOW DO YOU FEEL?

...MOM?

I DON'T LIKE THE WAY SHE'S STARING AT US.

ME EITHER.

MADAM...I'VE GOT **GOOD** NEWS... AND **BAD** NEWS. WHICH DO YOU WANT FIRST?

WHAT'S THE GOOD NEWS?

YOUR MOTHER **GAVE UP** DRINKING GIN & TONICS FOR NEW YEAR'S.

REALLY? THAT'S GREAT!

...WHAT'S THE BAD NEWS?

MOM! **WHAT** ARE YOU DOING?!

I GAVE UP GIN & TONICS. SO I TOOK UP A NEW HOBBY.

SMOKING CIGARS?!

I'M A CIGAR AFICIONADO.

CIGARS ARE "IN" RIGHT NOW. STYLISH CELEBRI-TIES HOLD THEM ON THE COVERS OF MAGAZINES. SMOKING A CIGAR MAKES PEOPLE SIT UP AND NOTICE.

YOUR HAIR'S ON FIRE.

MADAM & Eve

BY S. FRANCIS, H. DUGMORE & RICO

OKAY. TIME'S UP. EVERYONE OUT OF THE CAGE.

HEY! THEY'RE NOT SO GREAT!

YEAH. WE WANT OUR MONEY BACK!

SORRY. NO REFUNDS.

IF YOU ASK ME, SHE'S REALLY PUSHING THE ENVELOPE.

SEE THE GREAT WHITES
Only 10 Rand

Panel 1: THE PRESIDENT'S ON LINE 3, WINNIE.

Panel 2: HELLO ...NELSON?

WRONG PRESIDENT. GUESS AGAIN.

Panel 3: BILL! HOW ARE YOU? HOW'S EVERYTHING AT THE WHITE HOUSE?

DON'T ASK.

Panel 4: WINNIE... I NEED YOUR ADVICE.

DENY EVERYTHING.

Panel 5: BILL CALLS WINNIE FOR ADVICE...

IT'S A NIGHTMARE, WINNIE. THE WHOLE WHITE HOUSE IS COLLAPSING AROUND ME.

Panel 6: I'M SORRY TO CALL YOU SO LATE, BUT I'M AT MY WITS END. THE STRAIN IS TAKING ITS TOLL.

Panel 7: THIS IS A MAJOR CRISIS, WINNIE. NOT JUST FOR THE U.S. PRESIDENCY... BUT FOR DEMOCRACY AND THE ENTIRE FREE WORLD!

Panel 8: ... SO. WHAT ARE YOU WEARING RIGHT NOW? SOMETHING LACEY?

NOT NOW, BILL.

Panel 9: WINNIE-- THIS SCANDAL COULD RUIN ME! WHAT AM I GOING TO DO? DO WHAT I DID!

Panel 10: ... BOLDLY STARE YOUR ACCUSERS RIGHT IN THE EYE AND DENY ALL CHARGES!

Panel 11: EASY FOR YOU TO SAY, WINNIE! YOU HAD THOSE SHINY BLACK SUNGLASSES WITH THE DIAMOND STUDS!

Panel 12: BY THE WAY. I LOVE THOSE SUNGLASSES ON YOU. THEY'RE SO...SO... DOMINEERING...

BILL, TRY AND STAY FOCUSED.

BILL CALLS WINNIE FOR ADVICE...

WHAT CAN I DO, WINNIE? THESE TWO WOMEN ARE TRYING TO GET ME IMPEACHED!

≈SIGH≋ SOMETIMES I WISH THEY WOULD BOTH JUST... **DISAPPEAR.**

HEY! YOU STILL HAVE THAT FOOTBALL CLUB?

FORGET IT, BILL.

BILL -- ARE YOU SURE YOU'RE NOT IN DENIAL?

WINNIE -- I'M INNOCENT!

SURE, I INVITED THOSE WOMEN INTO MY PRIVATE OFFICE! BUT ALL I DID WAS TEACH THEM TO PLAY MY **SAXOPHONE!**

≈SIGH≋ I ALWAYS KNEW MY SAXOPHONE WOULD GET ME INTO BIG TROUBLE.

BILL... I'VE GOT ANOTHER CALL.

AND, IN OTHER NEWS...

SCIENTISTS HAVE DISCOVERED THAT, AFTER STUDYING NELSON MANDELA, PW BOTHA AND NOW FW DE KLERK...

...THAT SOMETHING IN THE SOUTH AFRICAN AIR SEEMS TO INCREASE ROMANTIC CAPABILITIES OF AGEING POLITICIANS.

BETTY. CALL AIR FORCE ONE. I'M LEAVING FOR SOUTH AFRICA IMMEDIATELY!

...SIR?

FIRST NELSON MANDELA... THEN PW BOTHA... AND NOW FW DE KLERK.

SCIENTISTS NOW BELIEVE THAT SOMETHING IN THE SOUTH AFRICAN AIR IS CAUSING ELDERLY POLITICAL PERSONALITIES TO BECOME INFATUATED WITH YOUNGER PARTNERS.

HOW DOES IT HAPPEN? WHO WILL BE THE NEXT VICTIM TO SUCCUMB TO THE MYSTERY INFATUATION DISEASE?

IT'S TRUE. PETER MOKABA AND I ARE IN LOVE.

MRS. VERWOERD! MRS. VERWOERD!

MADAM & EVE

ART APPRECIATION

BY S. FRANCIS, H. DUGMORE & RICO

ANDY WARHOL

SALVADOR DALI

EDVARD MUNCH

PIET MONDRIAN

JACKSON POLLOCK

GOOD MORNING, MADAM.

PABLO PICASSO

MADAM & Eve

BY S. FRANCIS, H. DUGMORE & RICO

WE'RE LEARNING ABOUT "EXPRESSIONS" AT SCHOOL. WHAT DOES "PASSING THE BUCK" MEAN?

GO ASK SOMEONE ELSE.

SEE? I SAID..."GO ASK SOMEONE ELSE." THAT'S AN EXAMPLE OF "PASSING THE BUCK," GET IT?

NO! IT DOESN'T MAKE ANY SENSE! NO BUCK WAS EVER PASSED! WHERE'S THE BUCK? SHOW ME THE BUCK!!

THERE IS NO BUCK! IT'S AN EX-PRESSION!

LOOK, HERE'S A BUCK. I PASS IT TO YOU, RIGHT?

NOW YOU PASS IT BACK TO ME.

SORRY. THE BUCK STOPS HERE.

THANKS. I THINK I UNDERSTAND "EXPRESSIONS" NOW.

WHO SAYS EDUCATION'S FREE IN THE NEW SOUTH AFRICA?

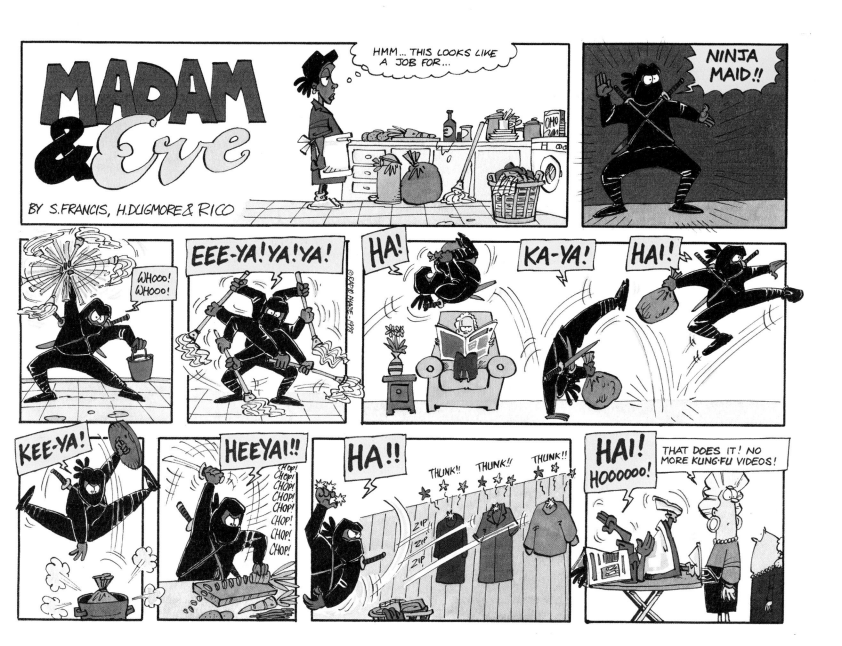

MADAM & Eve — Art Appreciation II

BY S. FRANCIS, H. DUGMORE & RICO

ROY LICHTENSTEIN

I LIKED THE OLD COUCH BETTER.

HENRY MOORE

HENRI ROUSSEAU

WHISTLER

MICHELANGELO

MADAM & Eve

THE TWELVE DAYS OF CHRISTMAS
BY S. FRANCIS, H. DUGMORE & RICO

On the twelfth day of Christmas, my true love gave to me... twelve beggars begging...
(Signs: NO FOOD! NO HOME, Please Help NO MONEY, NO JOB NO FOOD!)

Eleven markets crashing...

Ten jailbirds jumping...

Nine taxis fighting...

Eight cars a-hijacked...

Seven hawkers hawking...

Six people lying...
TRUTH & RECONCILIATION COMMISSION

Five gol-den rings!
CAPE TOWN 2004

Four gin & tonics...

Three staring workers...

Two mielie ladies...
MIELLLIES!!

And a GORILLA to keep them all away!

MERRY CHRISTMAS!
Madam & Eve

MADAM & Eve

BY S. FRANCIS, H. DUGMORE & RICO

"THE NIGHT BEFORE CHRISTMAS"... BY THANDI MSWELI.

'TWAS THE NIGHT BEFORE CHRISTMAS... AND ALL THROUGH THE ZOO... NOT A CREATURE WAS STIRRING...

...NOT EVEN A GNU.

FATHER CHRISTMAS'S SLEIGH WAS JUST FLYING OVER... ACCIDENTALLY HE HIT THE GORILLA ENCLOSURE.

CRASH!

"NOT **AGAIN**!" BELLOWED MAX, "HOW DARE SOMEONE TRY IT! WHY CAN'T A GORILLA GET SOME PEACE AND SOME QUIET?!"

THE NAME'S FATHER CHRISTMAS ...NO NEED TO BE RUDE! MY SLEIGH JUST CRASH-LANDED, I DON'T MEAN TO INTRUDE.

AND ALL THE ZOO ANIMALS FROM REPTILE TO BEAST INSISTED HE STAY FOR A BIG CHRISTMAS FEAST.

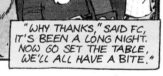

"WHY THANKS," SAID FC, IT'S BEEN A LONG NIGHT. NOW GO SET THE TABLE, WE'LL ALL HAVE A BITE."

SO THE LIONS DID COOK AND THE LEOPARDS DID CARVE, THERE WAS PLENTY OF FOOD, (SO NO ONE WOULD STARVE.) THE MENU WAS SIMPLE AND EASY TO MAKE...

...REINDEER TARTARE AND SANTA CLAUS STEAK!

WAIT A MINUTE ?!" ARE YOU TELLING US... THEY ATE FATHER CHRISTMAS?!

COOL, HEY?

JUST KIDDING! ACTUALLY THEY ALL HAD A GREAT TIME!

...AND THEY HEARD HIM EXCLAIM AS HE DROVE OUT OF SIGHT, MERRY CHRISTMAS SOUTH AFRICA, AND TO ALL A GOOD NIGHT!!

...THE END. ...AND HAPPY HOLIDAYS!

I'M GETTING REALLY WORRIED ABOUT THAT KID.

89

MADAM & Eve

BY S.FRANCIS, H.DUGMORE & RICO

MADAM & Eve

BY S. FRANCIS, H. DUGMORE & RICO

TWEET!!

STOP PLAYING! YOU WERE OFFSIDE!!

WHAT ARE YOU, BLIND?!

NO ARGUING WITH THE REFEREE! YOU GET A YELLOW CARD!

CAN YOU BELIEVE THIS? SHE GIVES ME A YELLOW CARD.

IS THAT GOOD OR BAD?

AND YOU MRS GOLDBERG! USE YOUR FOOT TO KICK THE BALL, NOT YOUR WALKER!

OH--YOU'RE SO SMART YOU CAN DO BETTER?

OW!!

STOMP!

HOW COME YOU GOT A YELLOW CARD? I NEVER GET ANY CARDS!

I TOLD YOU WE SHOULD'VE PLAYED RUGBY!

SO WHERE'S THE BALL?

YOU'RE HOLDING IT!

NEVER AGAIN.

HAVING FUN?

WOMEN'S SENIOR CITIZENS SOCCER LEAGUE

MADAM & Eve

BY S. FRANCIS, H. DUGMORE & RICO

WHUMP!!

UH-OH.

HOLD ON, I'M TAKING EVASIVE ACTION!!

SCREECH!!

VROOOM!!

IT'S A RED LIGHT! WE'RE TRAPPED!!

SCREECH!!

SIGH
...ROLL DOWN THE WINDOW.

I'M TELLING YOU, MOM. THESE PAMPHLET GUYS GET MORE PERSISTENT EVERY DAY.

MADAM & Eve

BY S. FRANCIS, H. DUGMORE & RICO

EVE'S GAME RESERVE
Only 10 Rand

ARE YOU CRAZY?! THIS IS OUR BACK YARD!!

QUIET. YOU'LL SCARE THE ANIMALS.

THIS I'VE GOT TO SEE. HERE'S OUR MONEY.

OKAY. SINGLE FILE AND STAY CLOSE TO ME.

CAREFUL WHERE YOU WALK. THESE WATERS COULD BE CROCODILE INFESTED.

THIS IS OUR SWIMMING POOL!

IT'S RUMOURED THAT THIS GIANT WALL WAS BUILT BY A LOST CIVILIZATION.

THAT'S OUR SECURITY FENCE!

SHHH! QUIET! THERE'S SOMETHING MOVING IN THOSE BUSHES!

((RUSTLE)) ((RUSTLE))

STAY BACK! IT'S A LION!!

THAT'S OUR NEIGHBOUR'S CAT.

MIAOU?

AND A GIANT WATER BUFFALO!! ...WE'RE TRAPPED!

WOOF! WOOF! WOOF!

THAT DOES IT! THIS IS THE STUPIDEST GAME RESERVE I HAVE EVER SEEN!

LET'S GO INSIDE!

TOURISTS...THEY'RE NEVER SATISFIED.

AM I ON YET?

95

MADAM & Eve

BY S. FRANCIS, H. DUGMORE & RICO

AH! THIS IS THE LIFE, HEY EVE? THERE'S NOTHING BETTER THAN A CRUISE ON A LARGE OCEAN LINER.

UH-OH.

THE *TITANIC*?!! WE'RE ON THE *TITANIC*?!! QUICKLY! WE'VE GOT TO WARN THE CAPTAIN!

SOMEONE CALL ME?

... MOM ??!

THAT'S ... "CAPTAIN MOM" TO YOU.

EXCUSE ME, CAPTAIN. WE NEED YOU ON THE BRIDGE! WE'RE HEADING STRAIGHT FOR --

... A GIANT *ICEBERG*?!

... ACTUALLY SIR, IT'S A GIANT GIN & TONIC.

AAAAH!! ABANDON SHIP!!

CRACK!!!

NO NEED TO PANIC! I'LL TAKE CARE OF THAT GIN & TONIC PERSONALLY!

MOM! YOU'VE BEEN IN THE BATHTUB FOR TWO HOURS! WHAT ARE YOU DOING IN THERE?!

CHANGING HISTORY!

LOOK MOM. I GOT YOU A PRESENT.

WHAT IS IT?

IT'S A **SNORKEL**! ...YOU KNOW, FOR THE POOL!

HAPPY VALENTINE'S DAY

PW BOTHA

DEAR VALENTINE, YOU ARE A TOTAL ONSLAUGHT ON MY HEART. LET'S CROSS THE RUBICON TOGETHER.

FW DE KLERK

DEAR VALENTINE, WORDS CANNOT EXPRESS HOW MUCH I LOVE YOU. PS: GIVE MY BEST TO YOUR HUSBAND.

BILL CLINTON

DEAR VALENTINE, ROSES ARE RED VIOLETS ARE BLUE. I'LL DENY EVERYTHING AND SO SHOULD YOU.

MADAM & Eve

BY S. FRANCIS, H. DUGMORE & RICO

"I AM A LIBRA
YOU ARE A TAURUS.
HAPPY VALENTINE'S DAY
I WANT A DIVORCE.

SIGNED...FW DE KLERK."

DOESN'T WORK.
YOU CAN'T RHYME
TAURUS
WITH
DIVORCE.

WILL
YOU **STOP**
PICKING ON
FW DE KLERK
ALREADY?!

IT'S HIS
OWN FAULT.
HE'S NOT
ON MY
LIST.

LIST?
WHAT
LIST?

MY LIST OF POLITICIANS
AND CELEBRITIES.
THEY **PAY** ME EVERY
WEEK TO INSURE THAT
WE DON'T MAKE
FUN OF THEM.

YOU'RE ACCEPTING
MONEY TO KEEP THEIR
NAMES OUT OF THIS
CARTOON?!!

THAT'S
RIGHT.
...SO?

THAT'S EXTORTION!
... **BLACKMAIL!**

I PREFER TO
CALL IT...
"ANTI-SATIRE
INSURANCE."

UH-OH.
I SEE JESSIE DUARTE
DIDN'T MAKE HER
PAYMENT THIS WEEK.

LOOK! IT'S THE
JESSIE DUARTE
SCHOOL OF
DRIVING!

The JESSIE DUARTE
DRIVING
SCHOOL

SCREECH!
CRASH!
BASH!

SORRY, JESS.
BUT LET'S GET
THOSE PAYMENTS
IN ON TIME,
OKAY?

FREEZE! LIPOSUCTION
POLICE! UP AGAINST THE
WALL AND SPREAD
'EM!!

LET ME GUESS...
"FELICIA"?

HER
CHEQUE
BOUNCED.

©RAPID PHASE · 1998

MADAM & Eve

BY S. FRANCIS, H. DUGMORE & RICO

...AND IN OTHER NEWS, THE RACE FOR THE **NEW TV CHANNEL LICENSE** IS HEATING UP AS THE **IBA** CONTINUES TO INTERVIEW POTENTIAL CANDIDATES.

OKAY. WHO'S THE NEXT APPLICANT?

HI. WE REPRESENT THE MADAM & EVE CHANNEL.

AS YOU CAN SEE, WE'RE A NON-RACIAL CONSORTIUM WHO BELIEVE IN **BLACK EMPOWERMENT**. THIS IS EVE.

HI.

THE MADAM & EVE CHANNEL BELIEVES IN ENTERTAINMENT, ENTERTAINMENT, ENTERTAINMENT! HERE'S A FEW OF OUR TENTATIVELY SCHEDULED PROGRAMMES!

SHOP 'TIL YOU DROP!

STARRING SUBURBAN CONSUMER EXPERT, GWEN ANDERSON!

THE SHOW THAT GETS SOUTH AFRICANS SHOPPING!

YOUR OWN BUSINESS

...FEATURING EVE SISULU.

START YOUR OWN TV STATION
Only 10 Rand

GIN 'N SPIN

...A FAST-PACED QUIZ SHOW WHERE CONTESTANTS WIN VALUABLE PRIZES AND DRINK LOTS OF GIN & TONICS!

PLUS

LOTS OF FAILED AMERICAN SITUATION COMEDIES WE CAN GET REALLY **CHEAP**!

HAHAHA HOHOHOHO HEEHEEHEE HAHAHA

...AND BY THE WAY. DID I MENTION THE BLACK EMPOWERMENT THING?

...SEVERAL TIMES. THANK YOU. WE'LL LET YOU KNOW.

NEXT APPLICANT! THE **MIELIE CHANNEL**!

UH-OH.

WELCOME TO OUR LIVE STAGE SHOW... **THE FULL MONTY-- SOUTH AFRICAN STYLE!!**

GIRLS -- SAY HELLO TO OUR FIRST DANCER... WE CALL HIM... **THE SMOOTH CRIMINAL!**

CLAP CLAP CLAP
CLAP CLAP CLAP
CLAP CLAP

WOW. CHECK OUT HIS UZI.

WHO WANTS TO BE HIJACKED?!

ME! ME!

THE FULL MONTY

♫ ...HOT STUFF ♫

LEND ME SOME MONEY. I WANT TO TIP ONE OF THE DANCERS!

ALL I HAVE IS A FIFTY RAND NOTE.

I'LL TAKE IT!

MOM! DON'T TELL ME YOU'RE SHOVING A WHOLE FIFTY BUCKS IN THAT GUY'S G-STRING!

OF COURSE NOT!

I'LL MAKE CHANGE.

MOM!

HERE'S MY MONEY!

MINE TOO!

THE FULL MONTY! Only 10 Rand

THIS IS MONTY.

THE FULL MONTY

WANT ANOTHER SANDWICH, MONTY?

NO THANKS. I'M FULL.

THE FULL MONTY

I SAY WE KILL THEM BOTH.

THE FULL MONTY

MADAM & Eve

BY S.FRANCIS, H.DUGMORE & RICO

MADAM! YOUR NEW FINANCIAL ADVISOR'S HERE!

SAWUBONA.

LET'S TALK FUTURES!

...A SANGOMA?

HE COMES HIGHLY RECOMMENDED. HE GOT OUT OF GOLD A WEEK BEFORE THE CRASH.

I WILL NOW ROLL THE BONES... AND MY ANCESTORS WILL SPEAK TO ME.

((RATTLE))
((RATTLE RATTLE))

YES. THE MISTS OF THE WORLD MARKETS ARE CLEARING...

QUICKLY! WHAT DO YOU SEE?!

I SEE... AN UPWARD TURN ON THE HONG KONG MARKET WHICH SHOULD IMPACT FAVOURABLY ON THE DECLINING GOLD INDEX. ALTHOUGH EQUITIES WILL CONTINUE TO BE HAMMERED BY OPPORTUNISTIC FUTURES DEALERS, THE EROSION OF INVESTOR CONFIDENCE SHOULD SUBSIDE ...

...ALLOWING FOR AN UNEXPECTED UPTURN IN THE RAND TO DOLLAR VALUE WITH A KNOCK-ON EFFECT ON MARKET SENTIMENT.

WHAT ARE YOU SAYING?

MY ANCESTORS ARE FEELING BULLISH. THEY SAY "PUT EVERYTHING INTO UNIT TRUSTS AND PLATINUM."

NOT SO FAST! WHAT DO THE BONES SAY ABOUT ME?!

YOU WILL GO ON A LONG TRIP, DRINK LOTS OF GIN AND MEET A TALL DARK STRANGER.

THIS GUY'S GOOD.

I'M CALLING MY STOCK BROKER!!

MADAM & Eve

BY S. FRANCIS, H. DUGMORE & RICO

EVE'S CASABLANCA CASINO

OF ALL THE NEWLY-LICENSED GIN JOINT CASINOS IN ALL OF SOUTH AFRICA -- THEY HAVE TO WALK INTO MINE.

EVE. SO WE MEET AGAIN! ...I SEE YOU GOT YOUR CASINO LICENSE.

YES. AND IF YOU'RE LOOKING FOR ACTION... YOU'VE COME TO THE RIGHT PLACE. WHAT CAN I DO FOR YOU?

LET'S JUST SAY... WE'RE INTERESTED IN BLACK JACK.

RIGHT OVER THERE.

HEY JACK! SOMEONE HERE TO SEE YOU.

BE RIGHT THERE, MISS SISULU.

ER, FORGET "BLACK JACK." WHAT ELSE HAVE YOU GOT FOR ENTERTAINMENT?

DO YOU LIKE BACHARACH?

YOU MEAN... "BACCARAT."

NO, I MEAN BACHARACH. ...BURT BACHARACH. HE WORKS HERE NOW.

GO AHEAD BURT, ...PLAY IT. ...PLAY IT AGAIN.

WHAT THE WORLD NEEDS NOW... IS LOVE, SWEET LOVE...

THAT DOES IT! THIS HAS GOT TO BE THE SILLIEST, DUMBEST, MOST IDIOTIC CARTOON I'VE EVER BEEN IN! COME ON, MOM. WE'RE LEAVING!!

WAIT! COME BACK! YOU HAVEN'T SEEN THE ONE-ARMED BANDIT YET!

MADAM! WE'VE BEEN **ROBBED!!**

RIGHT FROM UNDER OUR NOSES! ONE MOMENT THEY WERE THERE... THE NEXT MOMENT THEY WERE GONE!

CALM DOWN, EVE. WHAT HAPPENED?

SOMEBODY STOLE THE **PUNCHLINES** TO THIS WEEK'S CARTOONS!

YOU'RE KIDDING.

AND THE GOVERNMENT SAYS 'CRIME STATISTICS ARE **DECREASING**!

WHAT'S GOING ON?

SOMEBODY STOLE THE **PUNCHLINES** TO ALL OF THIS WEEK'S CARTOONS!

THAT'S IMPOSSIBLE.

IS IT? GO AHEAD... TRY AND SAY SOMETHING FUNNY.

UH... ...LIKE WHAT?

SEE? THAT DOES IT! I'M CALLING THE POLICE.

THANK GOODNESS YOU'RE HERE, OFFICERS. SOMEBODY **STOLE** THE **PUNCHLINES** TO THIS WEEK'S CARTOONS.

I SEE. ONE MOMENT THEY WERE HERE... THEN THEY WERE **GONE!**

...AND **WHERE** WAS THE LAST TIME YOU SAW THESE "PUNCHLINES"?

WE USUALLY KEEP THEM IN THE FOURTH PANEL. FOLLOW ME.

NOTHING FUNNY HERE AT ALL.

NOW DO YOU BELIEVE ME?!

MADAM & EVE

BY S. FRANCIS, H. DUGMORE & RICO

HOW WOULD YOU LIKE TO HELP ME WITH MY HOMEWORK?

IT'S A SCHOOL PROJECT ON PIRATES. GO AHEAD, NAME A PIRATE. I KNOW, I KNOW. LONG JOHN SILVER, RIGHT?

BUT THERE ARE LOTS OF OTHERS... BLACK MORGAN, BLACKBEARD, BLACK SPOT, BLACK DOG...

I BET YOU DIDN'T KNOW SO MANY BLACK GUYS WERE PIRATES.

IF YOU WERE A PIRATE, YOU'D PROBABLY BE CALLED "BLACK EDITH."

BLACK EDITH!! HAHAHA!! HEEHEEHEE!! HOOHOOHOO!!

SHIVER ME TIMBERS--IT'S BLACK EDITH! SWAB THE DECKS--IT'S BLACK EDITH! DON'T DRINK ALL THAT RUM -- SAVE SOME FOR BLACK EDITH!! HAHAHA!! HEEHEEHEE!! HOOHOOHOO!!

PRETTY FUNNY, HEY?! THANKS FOR YOUR HELP. SEE YOU TOMORROW.

IT'S AT TIMES LIKE THESE THAT ONE REALLY APPRECIATES BEETHOVEN'S NINTH AT FULL VOLUME.

Panel 1:
EVE... WHERE DO YOU GO ON YOUR DAY OFF?

ER..., NOWHERE.

Panel 2:
COME ON. YOU'RE GONE ALL DAY.

WELL... THE TRUTH IS... I'VE BEEN DOING A LITTLE FREELANCE DOMESTIC WORK IN THE NEIGHBOURHOOD.

Panel 3:
...WHAT?

Panel 4:
YOU'VE BEEN SEEING ANOTHER MADAM BEHIND MY BACK?!!

TWO-TIMER.

Panel 5:
MADAM! IT'S NOT SUCH A **BIG DEAL**! I'VE JUST BEEN WORKING ON MY DAY OFF!

YES!...WORKING FOR **ANOTHER MADAM**!

Panel 6:
SO TELL ME. **WHO** IS SHE?

SHE LIVES JUST DOWN THE STREET. YOU DON'T KNOW HER.

Panel 7:
DOES SHE... PAY YOU **MORE** THAN I DO?

WELL... ACTUALLY, YES. SHE DOES.

Panel 8:
CHOKE SOB!

NOW LOOK WHAT YOU'VE DONE!

Panel 9:
TELL ME EVERYTHING ABOUT THIS PERSON YOU WORK FOR ON THURSDAYS.

WHAT DO YOU WANT TO KNOW?

Panel 10:
FIRST OF ALL... WHAT DOES SHE CALL **YOU**?

WHAT ELSE? SHE CALLS ME **EVE**.

Panel 11:
I SEE. AND WHAT DO YOU CALL HER?

I CALL HER... **MADAM**.

Panel 12:
CHOKE SOB

GO AHEAD! WHY DON'T YOU JUST TAKE A KNIFE AND **STICK IT IN HER BACK**?!

116

I SAY WE **FOLLOW** EVE AND FIND OUT WHO SHE WORKS FOR ON HER "DAY OFF".

GOOD IDEA.

SO FAR, SO GOOD.

THIS WAS A GOOD IDEA...TO FOLLOW EVE ON HER "DAY OFF" AND FIND OUT WHO SHE WORKS FOR.

LOOK! IT'S NELSON MANDELA!

THE OLD "LOOK-IT'S NELSON MANDELA TRICK" ...AND **WE** FELL FOR IT.

IT'S MY MAID, DOCTOR. I JUST DISCOVERED... SHE'S BEEN WORKING ON HER DAY OFF... FOR **ANOTHER MADAM!**

I SEE.

MRS. ANDERSON... IF IT UPSETS YOU... WHY DON'T YOU JUST GIVE YOUR MAID A **RAISE**? MAYBE THEN SHE WON'T HAVE TO WORK ON HER DAY OFF.

A RAI... A RAI...

A **RAISE**. TRY AND SAY IT WITH ME.

U.S. SECRET SERVICE, MA'AM. CONGRATULATIONS! YOUR ROAD HAS BEEN SELECTED AS ONE OF THE STREETS BILL CLINTON'S MOTORCADE WILL PASS BY.

WOW.

WE'LL, OF COURSE, HAVE TO CUT DOWN ALL YOUR TREES.

HUH?

...POTENTIAL HIDING PLACES FOR SNIPERS.

OH.

WE'LL ALSO HAVE TO DRAIN YOUR SWIMMING POOL.

DRAIN MY SWIMMING POOL?!

...POTENTIAL HIDING PLACE FOR SNIPERS POSING AS UNDERWATER DIVERS.

B222 B222 B222

RIGHT.

WE'LL ALSO HAVE TO RE-ARRANGE YOUR FURNITURE.

RE-ARRANGE MY FURNITURE?! WHY?!

MY PARTNER'S HOBBY IS INTERIOR DECORATING. HE THINKS HE CAN MAKE THE ROOM BRIGHTER.

OKAY PEOPLE! LET'S MOVE LIKE WE'VE GOT A PURPOSE! GO! GO! GO!

SORRY FOR THE BLINDFOLDS. IT'S ROUTINE.

G✳#G AMERICANS.

120

MADAM & EVE

BY S. FRANCIS, H. DUGMORE & RICO

GOOD MORNING, MISTER McBRIDE.

YOUR MISSION — SHOULD YOU CHOOSE TO ACCEPT IT — IS TO EXPOSE ILLEGAL GUN RUNNING... BY GOING UNDERCOVER IN MOÇAMBIQUE, POSING AS A GUN RUNNER YOURSELF WITHOUT THE GOVERNMENT'S KNOWLEDGE... AND EVENTUALLY GETTING CAUGHT RED-HANDED BY THE MAPUTO POLICE, WHO WILL **ARREST** YOU AND THROW YOU IN JAIL.

EXCUSE ME?

THIS TAPE WILL **SELF-DESTRUCT** IN FIVE SECONDS. GOOD LUCK, BOB.

PFFFT!!

WELCOME TO MOÇAMBIQUE, MISTER...?

McBRIDE. ROBERT McBRIDE.

IS YOUR TRIP BUSINESS... OR PLEASURE?

ACTUALLY, I'M HERE TO BUY SOME GUNS.

I MEAN **FUN!** HAVE A LITTLE **FUN!** DID I SAY "GUNS"?? I MEANT FUN. I'M HERE TO HAVE **FUN** ...AND GET A LITTLE SUN. FUN AND SUN. FORGET THE GUNS.

WOULD YOU STEP OUT OF YOUR VEHICLE, PLEASE, SIR?

DAMN. THESE GUYS ARE GOOD.

Robert McBride
SECRET AGENT

DON'T MISS NEXT WEEK'S THRILLING EPISODE:
ASSUME THE POSITION!

121

HELLO LOUIS. REMEMBER ME?

YOU!!

THAT'S RIGHT! THE RUGBY SPRINGBOK!

IT'S NOT ME YOU WANT! IT'S MANDELA! HE'S RUINING YOUR LIFE... NOT ME!

JUST KEEP WALKING. I HAVE A GUN IN MY POCKET POINTED RIGHT AT YOU.

WHO ARE YOU KIDDING? YOU HAVE HOOVES! YOU CAN'T PULL THE TRIGGER!

DARN..

SEE YOU IN COURT.

AND, IN OTHER NEWS, THE RUGBY SPRINGBOK MASCOT WAS ARRESTED YESTERDAY...

...THE SPRINGBOK WAS CAUGHT BY POLICE ATTEMPTING TO SMUGGLE GUNS ACROSS THE MOÇAMBICAN BORDER.

I'M INNOCENT, I TELL YOU!! I WAS FRAMED!!

THEY PUSHED HIM TOO FAR.

NO MONEY NO FOOD NO JOB

NO MONEY NO FOOD NO JOB

NO MONEY NO food NO JOB

MADAM & Eve

BY S. FRANCIS, H. DUGMORE & RICO

LOOK! IT'S THE EASTER BUNNY!

YOU JUST MISSED HIM. BUT HE LEFT YOU THESE CHOCOLATE EGGS!

FAST LITTLE FURBALL, ISN'T HE?

EVERY YEAR IT'S THE SAME THING! EVERYONE SEES THE EASTER BUNNY EXCEPT ME! OKAY...WHO EXACTLY SAW HIM...RAISE YOUR HAND.

GOOD! NOW WE'RE GETTING SOMEWHERE.

WHAT DID HE LOOK LIKE?

UH...HE WAS FURRY. HE...HAD FLOPPY EARS... BIG FEET... FLUFFY TAIL...

WAS HE WHITE OR BLACK?

GREY! HE HOPPED SO FAST, HE WAS JUST A BLUR.

WHO OWNS THE RIGHTS TO THE EASTER BUNNY-- SARFU OR THE NSC?

NEITHER! HE'S A FREE AGENT!

REALLY?! WHICH WAY DID HE GO? IF I CAN SIGN HIM UP, I CAN MAKE LOTS OF MONEY!

IN MY DAY, WE JUST SAID "THANK YOU," ATE THE CHOCOLATE, AND GOT SICK.

GREETINGS. I AM YOUR **SUPERFLEX COMPUTERISED HOME GYM** ... AS SEEN ON TV.

BEFORE WE BEGIN, PLEASE STEP ON MY **SCALE**. I WILL ANALYZE YOUR BODYWEIGHT AND DETERMINE YOUR OPTIMUM EXERCISE PROGRAMME.

= PLEASE STATE YOUR NAME.

ANDERSON, GWEN.

OOOH. WE LIKE OUR MILK TARTS DON'T WE, GWEN?

NOW CUT THAT OUT!!

GREETINGS. I AM THE **SUPERFLEX COMPUTERISED HOME GYM** ... AS SEEN ON TV. HOW CAN I HELP YOU?

WHAT CAN YOU DO TO REALLY **TIGHTEN** MY **BUTTOCKS?**

BOO!! AAAH!!

SPROING!

I MEAN PERMANENTLY.

EVE... PLEASE GO GET ME MY TAKKIES FROM THE CUPBOARD.

EVE ... WON'T YOU **RUN** UPSTAIRS AND FETCH MY HEADBAND.

THANKS ... AND WOULD YOU MIND **WALKING** TO THE KITCHEN AND GET MY MINERAL WATER?

I HEAR THESE COMEDY CLUB SHOWCASES FOR NEW COMEDIANS ARE VERY SUCCESSFUL.

OOO   OOO

LADIES AND GENTLEMEN... PLEASE WELCOME THE COMEDY STYLINGS... OF *EVE SISULU!!*

OOO

HI! HOW'S EVERYBODY DOING TONIGHT?

OOO   OO

CRASH!

UH, SIR... TWO WOMEN JUST **FAINTED** AT TABLE FOUR.

OOO   OOO

HAHAHA HAHAHA HA HA HAHAHA HA HAHA

SO THIS IS WHERE EVE SPENDS HER EVENINGS.-- DOING A STANDUP ACT AT A COMEDY CLUB.

OOO   OOO

BIG DEAL. LET HER HAVE HER LITTLE HOBBY. HOW BAD CAN IT BE? LET'S JUST ENJOY THE SHOW.

OOO   OOO

OKAY. HERE'S A GOOD ONE...

TWO MADAMS WALK INTO A BAR...

WAITER! DOUBLE GIN & TONIC!   MAKE THAT TWO!

OOO

BUT SERIOUSLY FOLKS... IT'S NOT EASY BEING A DOMESTIC WORKER.

OOO

WHY, LAST WEEK MY MADAM TOOK ME TO THE BEACH... SHE TOLD ME TO BRING MY BOARD.

OOO

I SAID: "SURFBOARD?" SHE SAYS: "NO -- THE IRONING BOARD!"

OOO

I DON'T GET IT.   ME NEITHER.

HAHAHA HEEHEE HOHOHOHO! HAHAHA   HAHA HA HA HAHA HA HA

MADAM & EVE

BY S. FRANCIS, H. DUGMORE & RICO

McBRIDE! YOU GOT A TELEPHONE CALL! SOMEONE NAMED "BILLY JEAN"!

ROBERT? IT'S MICHAEL JACKSON.

ABOUT TIME!

I LOVE YOU.

DON'T GIVE ME THAT "I LOVE YOU" CRAP! WHAT ABOUT OUR SECRET COUP?!

DON'T WORRY, IT'S STILL HAPPENING. WINNIE'S IN. BANTU'S IN. BOBBY'S IN...

WAIT A MINUTE. WHO'S BOBBY?!

MY SPECIAL PRE-TEEN FRIEND. I PROMISED HIM THE VICE-PRESIDENCY.

SO EVERYTHING'S STILL ON SCHEDULE.

YES. IF ONLY PEOPLE KNEW HOW CLOSE GENERAL MEIRING CAME TO FOILING OUR ENTIRE PLAN.

YES. THE MAN'S A GENIUS.

BY THE WAY. I WROTE A SONG ABOUT WHAT WE'RE DOING. TELL ME WHAT YOU THINK.

UH-OH.

WE ARE THE WORLD ♫ ♫ WE TOPPLE GOVERNMENTS... ♫ ♫

MICHAEL!! WILL YOU FORGET THE MUSIC AND GET ME OUT OF THIS MOZAMBICAN PRISON?!

DON'T WORRY, I'VE GOT JOHNNIE COCHRAN ON YOUR CASE.

WOW. YOU THINK HE CAN BEAT IT?

♫ BEAT IT! ♫ ♫ JUST BEAT IT! ♫

THE NEXT TIME I PLOT A COUP, I'M GETTING ELTON JOHN.

Robert McBride
SECRET AGENT

DON'T MISS NEXT WEEK'S THRILLING EPISODE:
MOONWALK TO FREEDOM

YOU KNOW, EVE...

...WE DEFINITELY COULD USE MORE TREES IN OUR GARDEN.

YOU CAN SAY THAT AGAIN!

WHAT'S THIS YOU COOKED FOR DINNER, EVE?

I CALL IT... "TOMATO SURPRISE."

IT LOOKS LIKE A **BOILED TOMATO**. WHAT'S THE **SURPRISE**?

THE SURPRISE IS... I **FORGOT** TO GO **SHOPPING**. THAT'S ALL THERE IS.

THAT WENT BETTER THAN EXPECTED.

EVERYTHING IS IN READINESS, IGOR. THROW THE SWITCH!

YES, MASTER.

BZZZT!! BZZZT!!

LOOK, IGOR! IT'S **ALIVE**! OUR CREATION IS ALIVE!!

HAHAHAHAHA!

COULD HAVE FOOLED ME.

CAN'T YOU JUST WAKE ME UP AND SHOUT "GET BACK TO WORK" LIKE NORMAL PEOPLE?!

MADAM & Eve

BY S.FRANCIS, H.DUGMORE & RICO

BYE, MADAM. I KNOW YOU CAN MANAGE WITHOUT ME. I'LL SEE YOU AFTER THE LONG WEEKEND.

NOT SO FAST.

THAT'S A WATER PISTOL.

OKAY, EVE. YOU'RE RIGHT. GO AHEAD... TAKE OFF ANOTHER PUBLIC HOLIDAY. "FREEDOM DAY"... "FAMILY DAY"... "HERITAGE DAY"... "WORKERS' DAY"... WHERE DOES IT ALL END ?!!

BUT WHAT ABOUT US ?!! THAT'S RIGHT-- DID YOU EVER - JUST ONCE - THINK ABOUT THAT WHILE YOU'RE OFF HAVING FUN ON YOUR HOLIDAY ?! WHAT ABOUT US ?!!

WE'RE ALL ALONE HERE! ... BUT IT'S NOT JUST THE FACT THAT WE HAVE TO DO ALL THE COOKING, CLEANING AND WASHING OUR- SELVES. IT'S YOU, EVE !

©RICO PHASE-1998

WE MISS YOU, EVE! YOU'RE PART OF THE FAMILY! PLEASE -- JUST THIS ONE TIME -- DON'T GO! STAY! AND SPEND THIS WORKERS' DAY WITH US!

CHOKE

BYE, MADAM. I KNOW YOU CAN MANAGE WITHOUT ME. I'LL SEE YOU AFTER THE LONG WEEKEND.

TOLD YOU IT WOULDN'T WORK.

YOU WASH, I'LL DRY.

Panel 1: LISTEN TO WHAT CAME IN THE POST! "... CONGRATULATIONS! YOU ARE A GUARANTEED WINNER!"

Panel 2: YOU HAVE DEFINITELY WON EITHER:
1) A NEW CAR
2) A NEW TV
3) A NEW VCR
4) A SMALL ENVELOPE WITH SOMETHING IN IT.

Panel 3: I BET I WON THE NEW CAR!!

Panel 4: I LOVE OPTIMISM IN WHITE PEOPLE. / SHE'S RIGHT, MOM. YOU PROBABLY ONLY WON THE VCR!

Panel 5: I'M EDITH ANDERSON. THIS LETTER I RECEIVED SAYS I'M A GUARANTEED WINNER. / OF COURSE! WELCOME TO TIME SHARE PROMOTIONS.

Panel 6: AN OPEN DOOR! I'M FREE!! ...FREE!!

Panel 7: NO MORE TIME SHARE VIDEOS!! HAHAHAHAHA! / WAKE UP BOB! YOU LET ONE GET BY YOU!

Panel 8: SORRY ABOUT THAT. NOW WHERE WERE WE?

Panel 9: OKAY. SO WHEN DO I COLLECT MY GUARANTEED PRIZE?!

Panel 10: SOON. BUT FIRST...YOU'LL HAVE TO WATCH A SPECIAL VIDEO ON TIME SHARING.

Panel 11: A SPECIAL VIDEO ON TIME SHARING. HOW BAD CAN IT BE?

Panel 12: BY THE WAY... WE STRAP YOU IN FOR YOUR OWN PROTECTION.

YES, IT'S **SWAMPY GLEN** TIME SHARE FLATS! SORT OF NEAR THE OCEAN! ...SO BEAUTIFUL, YOU WON'T BE-LIEVE YOUR EYES!

...AND SPEAKING OF EYES... **YOURS** ARE GETTING HEAVY!! IN FACT, YOU ARE GETTING SLEEPY... **VERY SLEEPY**... ...SLEEPY...

YOU WILL BUY TIME SHARE... YOU WILL **BUY** TIME SHARE...

WE WILL BUY TIME SHARE...

SEE? THAT WASN'T SO BAD, WAS IT?

WE HEAR AND OBEY.

A TEST OF WILLS.

ARE YOU READY TO BUY TIME SHARE?

NO. I WANT MY GUARANTEED PRIZE!

NOTHING CAN MOVE EDITH ANDERSON.

ARE YOU READY TO BUY TIME SHARE?

NO. I WANT MY GUARANTEED PRIZE!

HER RESOLVE IS WITHOUT QUESTION.

NOW ARE YOU READY TO BUY TIME SHARE?!

NEVER! GIVE ME MY PRIZE!

UH-OH...

LOOK. A NICE TALL, ICE COLD GIN & TONIC.

MADAM! YOU'RE BACK!

THANK GOODNESS!

GWEN-- LISTEN TO ME! WHAT DID YOU SIGN?! DID YOU SIGN ANYTHING?!!

YOU'RE FREE TO GO. ...AND CONGRATULATIONS! YOU ARE NOW THE PROUD OWNERS OF A SWAMPY GLEN LEISURE PROPERTY!

...THANKS...FRED...

TIME SHARE?! YOU BOUGHT TIME SHARE?!!

THEY CRACKED HER LIKE A THREE MINUTE EGG.

THIS IS GREAT!! I BOUGHT TIME SHARE ON A SWAMP LAND! WHAT ELSE COULD POSSIBLY GO WRONG?!

© RAPID PHASE 1992

"...BEAUTIFUL SWAMPY GLEN TIME SHARE HOLIDAY FLATS WITH ROLLING HILLS, STUNNING VISTAS, BABBLING BROOKS..."

"... LOCATED BY A PICTURESQUE SEMI-DORMANT VOLCANO."

RUMBLE!

HI, AND WELCOME TO SWAMPY GLEN TIME SHARE LEISURE VILLAGE.

YOU MUST BE GWEN ANDERSON. THE HEAD OFFICE CALLED AND SAID YOU'D PROBABLY SHOW UP SOONER OR LATER.

... WE HERE AT SWAMPY GLEN PRIDE OURSELVES ON SERVICE. SO IF THERE'S ANYTHING I CAN DO TO MAKE YOUR STAY MORE ENJOYABLE, PLEASE DON'T HESITATE TO ASK.

THROW US A ROPE!!!

CITY PEOPLE. THEY'RE SO DEMANDING.

COME INSIDE! THIS IS YOUR TYPICAL SWAMPY GLEN TIME SHARE FLAT. RUSTIC ... YET COMFORTABLE. NATURAL ... YET...

BLAM! BLAM! BLAM!

SORRY ABOUT THAT. ...DAMN MOSQUITOES.

YOU SHOOT MOSQUITOES WITH GUNS HERE?

...ONLY THE BIG ONES.

MADAM! LOOK AT THIS!

"GRAND OPENING: LUYT'S FAMILY RESTAURANT. GOOD FOOD, GOOD PRICES, GOOD COMPANY."

SEE? I TOLD YOU LOUIS LUYT WOULD BOUNCE BACK! COME ON! LET'S GO IN!

HI, LOUIS! TABLE FOR THREE?

#6✗#6☞ OFF.

DID YOU HEAR ABOUT *LOUIS LUYT*? HE'S OPENING UP A CHAIN OF FAMILY RESTAURANTS.

YES, MISTER PRESIDENT.

AND CAN YOU BELIEVE IT? HE INVITED ME TO THE GRAND OPENING!

THE INVITATION IS CLEVER. IT LOOKS JUST LIKE A **COURT ORDER**.

UH...THAT IS A COURT ORDER, SIR.

WHAT?!!

HELLO WELCOME TO LUYT'S FAMILY RESTAURANT. I'M LOUIS **LUYT**. CAN I TAKE YOUR ORDER?

THIS LOOKS GOOD. I'LL HAVE THE "NEPOTISM BURGER."

THE **WHAT?!!**

...THE...ER, "NEPOTISM BURGER". IT'S RIGHT HERE ON THE MENU.

"NEPOTISM BURGER?!" I'M **FIRING** MY MENU CONSULTANT! WHO IS HE?!

IT'S YOUR SON-IN-LAW, SIR.

OH. THEN... GIVE HIM A WRITTEN WARNING AND PUT IT IN HIS FILE.

HE'S ALREADY HAD **FIVE**, SIR.

I STILL CAN'T BELIEVE LOUIS LUYT OPENED UP A FAMILY RESTAURANT.

LOOK. THERE HE IS!

MISTER LUYT? WE'RE READY TO ORDER NOW.

NO MAN IS MY MASTER!! I BOW TO NO ONE!!

UH...REMEMBER THAT "SERVICE" THING WE TALKED ABOUT, SIR?

JUDAS.

LOUIS LUYT'S NEW FAMILY RESTAURANT...

HERE YOU GO. ENJOY YOUR MEAL.

EXCUSE ME, MISTER LUYT. BUT... I ORDERED THE FISH... AND INSTEAD THEY BROUGHT ME THE STEAK.

MY OWN PEOPLE BETRAYED ME! THEY FOLDED! I CAN'T TRUST MY OWN PEOPLE!!

UH. NO PROBLEM. THE STEAK'S FINE.

ISN'T THIS EXCITING?! LOUIS LUYT OPENS UP A NEW RESTAURANT... AND WE'RE HERE ON OPENING NIGHT!!

LOOK OVER THERE! ISN'T THAT MLULEKI GEORGE -- THE GUY WHO FORCED LOUIS LUYT TO RESIGN?

...I WONDER WHAT HE'S HAVING?

PTOO! PTOO!

GOOD. AND DON'T FORGET THE BAKED POTATO.

GWEN & EVE

BY S. FRANCIS, H. DUGMORE & RICO

GREAT NEWS, MOM. EVE **BOUGHT** THE HOUSE NEXT DOOR! SHE'S NOT OUR MAID ANY MORE... SHE'S NOW OUR **NEIGHBOUR!**

YES, MADAM. THANKS TO MY NEW HIGH-PAYING GOVERNMENT JOB AND HOUSING ALLOWANCE!

BY THE WAY. CALLING ME MADAM COULD PERPETUATE A DISEMPOWERING CLASS-STATUS STEREOTYPE. PLEASE... CALL ME GWEN.

OKAY... GWEN!

HEY! WHO **SWITCHED** MY GIN & TONIC WITH **ORANGE JUICE**?

I DID, MOM. EXCESSIVE CONSUMPTION OF ALCOHOL CAN CAUSE A LOSS OF CONTROL. NOT TO MENTION HEART AND LIVER DISEASE.

OKAY! **WHAT THE HELL IS GOING ON HERE?!!**

WHY, WHAT DO YOU MEAN?

WAIT A MINUTE! ⸘GASP⸘...THAT GLAZED, SELF-RIGHTEOUS LOOK IN YOUR EYES! YOU'VE ALL BECOME... POLITICALLY CORRECT!!

YES, MOM! ...AND **YOU'RE NEXT!**

JOIN US. ...JOIN US!

NEVER!

THANDI! THANK GOODNESS! TELL ME **YOU'RE** NOT ONE OF THEM! ...MAKE FUN OF ME! DO SOMETHING TO **ANNOY** ME!

SORRY, THAT MIGHT BE CONSTRUED AS AGEISM, WHICH-ALTHOUGH I HATE TO GENERALISE-WOULD PERHAPS MAKE ME INSENSITIVE TO YOUTH-FULLY-CHALLENGED PEOPLE EVERYWHERE.

© RICO McROSE - 1998

⸘GASP⸘ AND THE MIELIE LADY! DON'T TELL ME THEY GOT **YOU** TOO?!!

...ONLY I'M NOT JUST "THE MIELIE LADY" ANY LONGER, EDITH. I AM, HOWEVER, THE OWNER OF "MIELIE WORLD", A SUCCESSFUL MAIZE AND VEGETABLE MICRO-ENTERPRISE FRANCHISE.

AAAAAAH!

⸘CHOKE⸘ NO! KEEP BACK!

I THINK YOUR MOTHER'S HAVING A BAD DREAM, MADAM.

PLEASE. CALL ME ...GWEN.

MADAM & Eve

BY S. FRANCIS, H. DUGMORE & RICO

DING DONG!

HI. EARLY BIRD CARTOON REPAIR. YOU CALLED US?

YES! AND YOU WERE SUPPOSED TO BE HERE BEFORE FRIDAY!

HMMM.

WELL. WHAT DO YOU THINK?

WERE THE PANELS STRUCK BY LIGHTNING?

NO!

DID YOU DROP THEM?

NO!

DID YOUR MAID TOUCH ANYTHING?

NO! THE PICTURE JUST WENT FUNNY!

THIS CARTOON ISN'T UNDER WARRANTY, IS IT?

NO! AND BEFORE YOU DO ANY WORK, I WANT A WRITTEN QUOTE!

OKAY. BUT WE'RE GOING TO HAVE TO TAKE IT BACK TO THE SHOP.

BACK TO THE SHOP?! THAT'S IMPOSSIBLE! WE HAVE NEWSPAPER COMMITMENTS TODAY!

I COULD GIVE YOU A "LOANER" CARTOON.

A LOANER?

HEY... TAKE IT OR LEAVE IT.

FINE! WHAT CHOICE DO WE HAVE?! WE'LL TAKE IT!

"Find out if they're staying for dinner.
I'll take some hay out of the freezer."

143

MADAM & Eve

BY S. FRANCIS, H. DUGMORE & RICO

MADAM--THIS IS JABU. HE'S AN INYANGA, A TRADITIONAL HEALER. I TOLD HIM YOU'VE BEEN SICK ALL WEEK. HE'S HERE TO MAKE YOU BETTER.

OKAY. OPEN YOUR MOUTH AND SAY: "NDIZA KUBHATALA NGE NKOZO ZE MALI."

I HAVE DIAGNOSED THAT YOU ARE BOTH SICK. THERE'S A LOT OF FLU GOING AROUND.

OUR OWN DOCTOR ALREADY TOLD US THAT!

HERE. I WANT YOU TO DRINK THIS SPECIAL POTION.

WHAT'S IN IT?

OH... ROOTS... ...HERBS... ...BARK...

...POWDERED BABOON LIVER...

VOMITING IS GOOD! IT REMOVES THE BAD GERMS!

SO. HOW DO YOU FEEL?

HOW DO I FEEL??!! I FEEL--

HEY! I FEEL BETTER!

ME TOO.

HERE. JUST SEND MY BILL TO MY MEDICAL AID.

THIS IS WHY I DON'T MAKE HOUSECALLS TO THE NORTHERN SUBURBS.

MADAM & Eve

BY S.FRANCIS, H.DUGMORE & RICO

TAPITA TAPITA TAPITA TAPITA TAPITA TAPITA TAPITA TAPITA
TAPITA TAPITA TAPITA TAPITA TAPITA TAPITA TAPITA TAPITA

CLICKETY CLICKETY CLICKETY CLICKETY
CLICKETY CLICKETY CLICKETY CLICKETY CLICKETY
CLICKETY

TAPITA TAPITA TAPITA TAPITA TAPITA TAPITA
TAPITA TAPITA TAPITA TAPITA

THIS "LORD OF THE DANCE" THING HAS REALLY CAUGHT ON.

IT NEVER FAILS. I ALWAYS GET BEHIND SOME LITTLE OLD LADY IN THE SUPERMARKET CHECK-OUT QUEUE.

EITHER THEY TRY TO PAY WITH AN UNAPPROVED CHEQUE... THEN ONE OF THE EMPLOYEES HAS TO RUN AND FIND THE MANAGER...

OR...THEY CAN'T FIND THEIR MONEY... AND RUMMAGE AROUND IN THEIR HANDBAG FOR TWENTY MINUTES...PULLING EVERYTHING OUT...

...MOM! WILL YOU HURRY UP?!!

MIND YOUR OWN BUSINESS.

LORD OF THE UNEMPLOYED

AND, IN OTHER NEWS, GINGER SPICE GERI HALLIWELL HAS *LEFT* THE HUGELY SUCCESSFUL ALL-GIRL POP GROUP.

THE SPICE GIRLS SAY THEY WILL BE HOLDING INTERNATIONAL AUDITIONS TO FIND A REPLACEMENT. WHOEVER GETS CHOSEN WILL BECOME AN INSTANT MILLIONAIRE.

TELL ME WHAT YOU WANT! WHAT YOU REALLY REALLY WANT! IF YA WANNA BE MY LOVER...

OI! GIRL POWER!

ABSOLUTELY NOT! WE ARE NOT FLYING TO ENGLAND SO YOU CAN AUDITION FOR THE SPICE GIRLS!

PLEASE, MADAM! IF THEY PICK ME, I'LL SPLIT THE MONEY 50-50!

BESIDES...THEY ALREADY HAVE A BABY SPICE, *SCARY* SPICE, *SPORTY* SPICE AND *POSH* SPICE. WHY DO THEY NEED *YOU*?

DOMESTIC SPICE.

SHE SINGS.. THEN CLEANS UP. I LIKE IT.

I'M BOOKING THE TICKETS.

ARE YOU FROM THE RECORD COMPANY? WE'RE HERE FOR THE SPICE GIRLS AUDITION.

AREN'T YOU TWO A LITTLE YOUTHFULLY-CHALLENGED TO BE SPICE-GIRLS?

BONK!

GIRL POWER!! MADAM!!

POSSIBLE
NEW
SPICE
GIRL
REPLACEMENTS

MADAM SPICE

DOMESTIC SPICE

OLD SPICE

MADAM & EVE

BY S. FRANCIS, H. DUGMORE & RICO

...AND IN OTHER NEWS, SCIENTISTS OF THE APARTHEID GOVERNMENT'S CHEMICAL WARFARE PROGRAMME -- FEARFUL OF SUBVERSIVE SATIRE -- HAVE ADMITTED DEVELOPING **POISONOUS** SUBSTANCES THAT ONLY AFFECT CARTOON CHARACTERS.

GAS MASKS
Only 20 Rand

HERE'S YOUR GIN & TONIC, MOTHER ANDERSON.

SNIFF SNIFF

I THINK MY GIN & TONIC MIGHT BE TOXIC.

NEVER MIND THAT. DOES THIS INK SMELL FUNNY TO YOU?

SLAM!!

ACK!! CHOKE!!

© RAPID PHASE 1998

PLOP!

TWO PLEASE.

GAS MASKS
Only 20 Rand

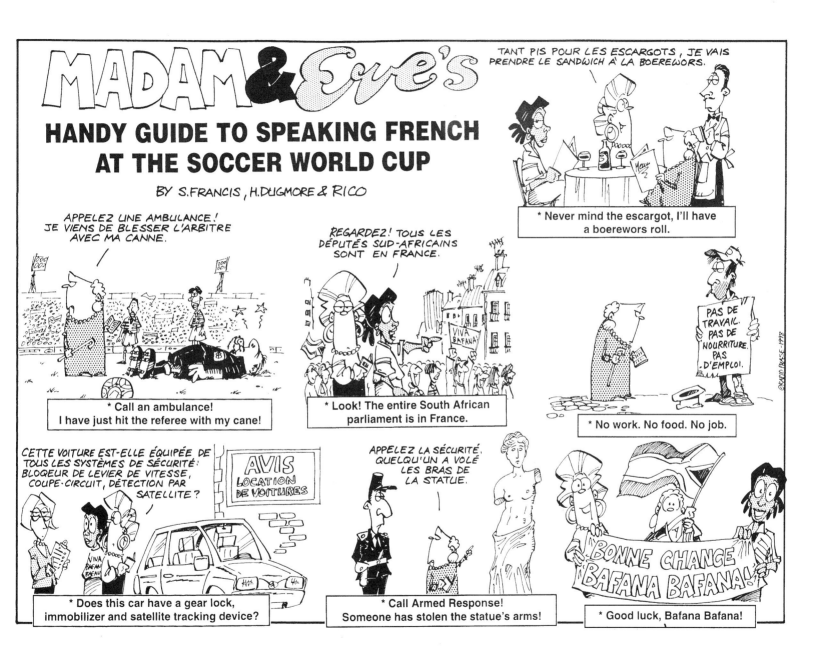

MADAM & Eve's

HANDY GUIDE TO SPEAKING FRENCH AT THE SOCCER WORLD CUP

BY S.FRANCIS , H.DUGMORE & RICO

TANT PIS POUR LES ESCARGOTS , JE VAIS PRENDRE LE SANDWICH À LA BOEREWORS.

* Never mind the escargot, I'll have a boerewors roll.

APPELEZ UNE AMBULANCE ! JE VIENS DE BLESSER L'ARBITRE AVEC MA CANNE.

* Call an ambulance! I have just hit the referee with my cane!

REGARDEZ ! TOUS LES DÉPUTÉS SUD-AFRICAINS SONT EN FRANCE.

* Look! The entire South African parliament is in France.

PAS DE TRAVAIL. PAS DE NOURRITURE. PAS D'EMPLOI.

* No work. No food. No job.

CETTE VOITURE EST-ELLE ÉQUIPÉE DE TOUS LES SYSTÈMES DE SÉCURITÉ: BLOQUEUR DE LEVIER DE VITESSE, COUPE-CIRCUIT, DÉTECTION PAR SATELLITE ?

AVIS LOCATION DE VOITURES

* Does this car have a gear lock, immobilizer and satellite tracking device?

APPELEZ LA SÉCURITÉ. QUELQU'UN A VOLÉ LES BRAS DE LA STATUE.

* Call Armed Response! Someone has stolen the statue's arms!

BONNE CHANGE BAFANA BAFANA!

* Good luck, Bafana Bafana!

DON'T YOU THINK IT'LL BE *EASIER* TO JUST GET YOUR CELLPHONE CHARGER REPAIRED?

IT'S NOT EASY GETTING HER TO MOVE OUT OF HER FAVOURITE CHAIR.

AND, IN SPORTS NEWS... TENSIONS ARE RUNNING EXTREMELY HIGH BETWEEN COACH PHILLIPE TROUSSIER AND THE PLAYERS OF BAFANA BAFANA.

COACH? PEOPLE DESCRIBE YOU AS ARROGANT... AUTOCRATIC AND TOTALLY IRRATIONAL. HOW DO YOU RESPOND TO THAT?

WHO SAYS ZESE THINGS -- YOU?! NO SOCCER FOR YOU!! YOU'RE OFF ZE TEAM!!

UH...SIR? I'M A REPORTER.

NO REPORTING FOR YOU! YOU'RE OFF THE NEWSPAPER!

COACH PHILLIPE TROUSSIER SEEKS PROFESSIONAL HELP...

YOU'VE GOT TO HELP ME, DOCTOR. PEOPLE SAY ZAT I AM ARROGANT, AUTOCRATIC AND IRRATIONAL.

WELL... IT'S JUST MY OPINION... BUT PERHAPS YOU SHOULD HAVE LET **BAFANA BAFANA** PLAY THEIR **OWN GAME** INSTEAD OF FORCING THEM INTO A EUROPEAN STYLE OF SOCCER.

FINE! I KEEL YOU NOW WITH MY BARE HANDS!

LET'S TALK ABOUT YOUR CHILD-HOOD.

COACH PHILLIPE TROUSSIER SEEKS PROFESSIONAL HELP...

COACH... I'M GOING TO SHOW YOU SOME INK BLOTS. I WANT YOU TO TELL ME WHAT YOU SEE?

AHÁ! ZIS IS A PICTURE OF DISLOYAL BAFANA BAFANA PLAYERS SNEAKING BACK INTO ZEIR HOTEL AFTER BREAKING ZE CURFEW AND DISREGARDING MY ORDERS.

AND ZIS ONE! A BUNCH OF SPORTS JOURNALISTS TALKING BEHIND MY BACK, SAYING I'M ARROGANT AND IRRATIONAL!

WHERE DID YOU GET ZEES?! WHO TOOK ZEES PHOTOS?!

UH-OH.

COACH PHILLIPE TROUSSIER SEEKS PROFESSIONAL HELP...

IT EEZ NOT FAIR, DOCTOR. I'M **NOT** ARROGANT AND IRRATIONAL! EVERYONE EEZ BLAMING ME FOR BAFANA BAFANA'S POOR PERFORMANCE IN ZE WORLD CUP.

I SEE...

...SO YOU'RE A SCAPEGOAT.

WHAT DID YOU JUST CALL ME?

A SCAPEGOAT. ...A PATSY. ...A FALL-GUY. ...A DUPE...

ZAT IS ENOUGH! I CHALLENGE YOU TO A DUEL! PISTOLS AT TWENTY PACES!

WELL, I SEE OUR TIME IS UP.

©RAPID PHASE - 1998   WWW.mg.co.za/mg/

COACH TROUSSIER SEEKS PROFESSIONAL HELP...

COACH -- I WANT TO GIVE YOU A WORD ASSOCIATION TEST. I'LL SAY A WORD... AND YOU SAY THE FIRST THING THAT COMES INTO YOUR MIND.

OKAY.

BAFANA-BAFANA!

DISLOYAL!

PLAYERS!

UNDISCIPLINED!

FANS!

UNGRATEFUL.

JOURNALISTS!

CRITICAL!

COACH!

ANGRY!

STOP!

GO!

C-CHOKE!

GRAB!

SECURITY!!

CALL!

©RAPID PHASE - 1998   WWW.mg.co.za/mg/

MADAM & Eve

BY S. FRANCIS, H. DUGMORE & RICO

LOOK AT THIS! EVERYONE'S TAKING ADVANTAGE OF THE FALLING **RAND**: "ATTENTION TOURISTS! SPEND A WEEK WITH A **REAL** SOUTH AFRICAN FAMILY! CALL NOW FOR BOOKINGS!!"

HEY! ISN'T THAT OUR ADDRESS?!

OKAY EVERYONE. BEFORE I SHOW YOU WHERE YOU'LL BE SLEEPING, I'LL BE TAKING YOU ON A TOUR OF THE HOUSE.

THIS IS THE KITCHEN. AND THESE... ARE REAL SOUTH AFRICAN... MADAMS.

WAS IST DAS... "MADAMS"?

"MADAMS"! YOU KNOW... WHITE EMPLOYERS? SHOP... WATCH TV? ...PAY LOW WAGES?

AAAAAAH!! ...MADAMS!!

ALRIGHT! HOLD IT **RIGHT THERE**!! WHAT'S GOING ON?!

ENTSCHULDIGUNG, EINEN MOMENT BITTE. ONE MOMENT PLEASE.

© RICO PHASE 1998

EVE...YOU ARE **NOT** HAVING A GROUP OF TOURISTS STAY IN MY HOUSE!!

THEY'RE PAYING ME IN DOLLARS, POUNDS AND DEUTSCHMARKS.

WE MAY BE SELLING OUT... BUT WE'RE SELLING OUT IN **DOLLARS**.

GET YOUR GIN & TONICS... ONLY TEN DOLLARS!

ANANT SINGH'S HERE TO SEE YOU, MISTER PRESIDENT.

GOOD. SEND HIM IN.

BAD NEWS, MISTER PRESIDENT. **MORGAN FREEMAN** AND **DENZEL WASHINGTON PASSED** ON PLAYING YOU IN "LONG WALK TO FREEDOM."

BOTH OF THEM?!

FRANKLY, SIR... WE'RE RUNNING OUT OF BLACK AMERICANS. BUT DON'T WORRY -- I'M GOING TO "PLAN B": WHITE AMERICANS THAT CAN PLAY BLACK SOUTH AFRICANS.

LIKE WHO?

PICTURE IT, SIR: DUSTIN HOFFMAN **IS** NELSON MANDELA.

ISN'T HE TOO SHORT?

SORRY, MISTER PRESIDENT. **MORGAN FREEMAN** DEFINITELY PASSED ON "LONG WALK TO FREEDOM". HE SAID HE JUST PLAYED A PRESIDENT IN "DEEP IMPACT." HE DOESN'T WANT TO GET TYPECAST.

BUT DON'T WORRY... MICHAEL JACKSON JUST CALLED. HE'S INTERESTED IN PLAYING YOU.

MICHAEL JACKSON?

WE'RE FREE AT LAST! I LOVE YOU!

OF COURSE, WE'D HAVE TO MAKE HIM BLACK AGAIN.

I'LL HAVE TO THINK ABOUT IT.

I FOUND HIM, MISTER SINGH! I FOUND YOUR "NELSON MANDELA" FOR "LONG WALK TO FREEDOM"!!

OKAY. GO AHEAD.

SO SHOUT IT FROM THE ROOFTOPS... WE'RE FREE... FREE AT LAST!

AMAZING! HE'S **PERFECT!** WHERE'D YOU FIND HIM? WHO IS HE?!

CAN YOU BELIEVE IT? IT'S **LEON SCHUSTER!**

FRANKLY, SIR. I THINK YOU COULD HAVE AT LEAST GIVEN HIM A CHANCE.

I'M THINKING OF BECOMING A POLITICAL CORRECTNESS CONSULTANT.

MY JOB WOULD BE TO ADVISE YOU AGAINST SAYING OR DOING SOMETHING POLITICALLY INCORRECT.

MY RATES ARE REALLY CHEAP. ...DO YOU WANT TO HIRE ME OR NOT?

ARE YOU CRAZY?!

YOU MEAN, "AM I MENTALLY CHALLENGED?" ...THAT WAS A FREE SAMPLE. NEXT TIME I'LL HAVE TO CHARGE YOU.

AND NOW, FOR MY NEXT TRICK...THE INCREDIBLE FLOATING CELLPHONE!

RING RING

RING RING

HELLO? DIDN'T I TELL YOU NEVER TO CALL ME WHEN I'M WORKING?

JUST MY LUCK. I HAVE TO GET A **MIME** AHEAD OF ME IN THE DOUBLE BANK SECURITY DOOR.

IN

164

MADAM & EVE

BY S. FRANCIS, H. DUGMORE & RICO

WELCOME TO THE COMMISSION FOR CONCILIATION, MEDIATION AND ARBITRATION. EDITH ANDERSON, YOUR CASEWORKER, WILL BE WITH YOU IN A MOMENT.

...PART TIME JOB.

LET'S SEE. ACCORDING TO THE DEPOSITION, A DISPUTE AROSE WHEN YOUR MAID -- WHO YOU'VE BEEN PAYING ONLY TEN RAND A DAY WITH NO OVERTIME -- WAS FIRED WITHOUT NOTICE OR WARNING.

HOW DARE YOU INCONVENIENCE THESE PEOPLE.!!

FINALLY! SOMEONE THAT CAN SEE OUR SIDE OF THE STORY.

YOU CAN'T BE TOO CAREFUL WITH THE HELP THESE DAYS. GIVE THEM A HAND... THEY TAKE THE WHOLE ARM!

RIGHT! LET'S GET DOWN TO THE FINAL JUDGEMENT. PUT ON THESE BOXING GLOVES.

BOXING GLOVES?!

YOUR WIFE AGAINST YOUR EX-MAID. WHOEVER WINS GETS A FAVOURABLE JUDGEMENT.

WHAT?!! THIS IS OUTRAGEOUS! HERE! SIX MONTHS BACK PAY!! DOUBLE BACK PAY! JUST LEAVE US ALONE.!!

SLAM!

WAIT! COME BACK! THERE'S STILL THE TEST OF FIRE AND WATER!

SO... YOU'RE EVE'S COUSIN.

HI, GWEN. WHAT'S ALL THIS I HEAR ABOUT "HONESTY WEEK." IT'S MY IDEA. FOR ONE WEEK EVERYONE IN THIS HOUSE HAS TO TELL THE HONEST **TRUTH**.

WELL...TO TELL YOU THE TRUTH, I'VE ALWAYS THOUGHT YOU HAD ABSOLUTELY NO DRESS SENSE. AND IN MY OPINION... YOU WEAR FAR TOO MUCH MAKE-UP.

YOU'RE A BUSYBODY AND A GOSSIP! OH YEAH?!! AND YOU HAVE A BIG NOSE!!

...AFTER LIVING NEXT DOOR FOR TWENTY YEARS, THEY JUST FOUND OUT THEY CAN'T STAND EACH OTHER.

G✱#@!!!

©RAPID PHASE - 1998   www.mg.co.za/mg/

WELL, WELL. IF IT ISN'T MY COFFEE-STEALING, DISH-CRACKING, CLOCK-WATCHING, EXCESSIVE BREAK-TAKING DOMESTIC **EMPLOYEE**.

AND IF IT ISN'T MY CELLPHONE-TALKING TV-WATCHING MALL-SHOPPING LUXURY-CAR-DRIVING EXCESSIVE-JEWELLERY-WEARING DOMESTIC **EMPLOYER**.

OKAY EVERYONE! "HONESTY WEEK" IS OFFICIALLY OVER!

©RAPID PHASE - 1998   www.mg.co.za/mg/

...AND MAY I SAY HOW MUCH I ENJOY WORKING FOR YOU. THE PLEASURE'S ALL MINE.

I WROTE A POEM TO CELEBRATE NELSON MANDELA'S 80th BIRTHDAY. WANT TO HEAR IT?

NO.

"DEAR MISTER PRESIDENT: ROSES ARE RED, VIOLETS ARE BLUE. YOU MAY BE EIGHTY, BUT MOTHER ANDERSON'S EIGHTY-TWO!

WELL? WHAT DO YOU THINK?

I HOPE NELSON MANDELA DOESN'T GET THAT GROUCHY WHEN HE TURNS 80!

CONGRATULATIONS, MISTER PRESIDENT. GIFTS TO CELEBRATE YOUR 80th BIRTHDAY ARE POURING IN FROM WORLD LEADERS.

BORIS YELTSIN SENT A SILVER TEA SERVICE FILLED WITH RUSSIAN CAVIAR.

FIDEL CASTRO SENT AN ENGRAVED HUMIDOR FILLED WITH CUBAN CIGARS.

AND THE GIRL IN THE BIKINI WHO JUMPED OUT OF THE CAKE, UH... THAT WAS FROM...

I KNOW. BILL CLINTON. IT WAS TATOOED ON HER STOMACH.

TA-DA!

HAPPY BIRTHDAY TO YOU! HAPPY BIRTHDAY TO YOU! ♫ HAPPY 80th BIRTHDAY PRESIDENT MANDEL-A HAPPY BIRTHDAY TO YOU!! ♫

BEST WISHES... FROM PRESIDENT BILL CLINTON!!

...AND THEN I GIVE HIM A MASSAGE. ...NOW CAN YOU LET ME PAST SECURITY?!

GOOD NEWS, MISTER PRESIDENT. IT'S ELTON JOHN ON THE LINE.

REALLY?

HE SAYS HE'LL BE HAPPY TO CHANGE THE WORDS TO ONE OF HIS SONGS TO FIT YOUR 80th BIRTHDAY CELEBRATION.

WHICH DO YOU LIKE BETTER? "WINNIE AND THE JETS?" "GROOT KROKODIL ROCK?" ...OR "SATURDAY NIGHT'S ALRIGHT FOR FIGHTING APARTHEID?"

TOUGH CHOICE. TELL HIM I'VE ALWAYS LIKED "ROCKET MAN".

HE SAYS HE'LL GET BACK TO YOU.

SEND PRESIDENT MANDELA A PERSONALISED BIRTHDAY GREETING Only 10 Rand

HERE'S MY MONEY. NOW WHAT?

SEND PRESIDENT MANDELA A PERSONALISED BIRTHDAY

HEY MISTER PRESIDENT! HAPPY 80th BIRTHDAY FROM MOTHER ANDERSON!!

CHRISTMAS AND NEW YEAR'S ARE ALSO AVAILABLE.

SEND PRESIDENT MANDELA A PERSONALISED BIRTHDAY

Only 350 more shopping days till NELSON MANDELA's 81st Birthday

MADAM & Eve

BY S.FRANCIS, H.DUGMORE & RICO

HI.

HAPPY MADAM'S DAY.

DID YOU SAY... "HAPPY MADAM'S DAY"?

THAT'S RIGHT! THE DOMESTIC WORKERS IN THE AREA HAVE OFFICIALLY PROCLAIMED THIS DATE AS "MADAM'S DAY."

FOR THE ENTIRE DAY, WE'RE NOT ALLOWED TO "BORROW" COFFEE OR SUGAR; VACUUM WHILE YOU WATCH TV; SECRETELY TRY ON YOUR CLOTHES, MAKE LONG DISTANCE PHONE CALLS, OR STIR YOUR TEA WITH OUR FINGERS.

AND HERE. I GOT YOU A CARD.

"ROSES ARE RED VIOLETS ARE BLUE THE BEST MADAM EVER HAS GOT TO BE YOU!"

BY THE WAY. IF THERE'S ANYTHING SPECIAL YOU WANT ME TO CLEAN, JUST LET ME KNOW.

SHE'S UP TO SOME-THING. ...BUT WHAT?!

I CAN'T TAKE IT. JUST GIVE HER A RAISE.

EVE SISULU, MASTER OF REVERSE PSYCHOLOGY.